About the Author

* * * * * * * * * * * * * * * * * * * *

Dr Michael Rafael Moreno, better known as Dr Mike, is a graduate of the University of California at Irvine and Hahnemann Medical School (now Drexel University). Following his residency at Kaiser Permanente in Fontana, California, Dr Mike moved to San Diego, where he now practises family medicine and sits on the board of the San Diego Chapter of the American Academy of Family Physicians.

In 2008 Dr Mike launched 'Walk with Your Doc' (http://www.walkwithyourdoc.com), which he participates in every Tuesday and Thursday morning before his workday begins. The programme began when Dr Mike offered to walk with a patient to motivate her to exercise, and has since grown into a thriving community.

Dr Mike takes pride in being viewed not only as a doctor, but also as a friend and confidant.

'We've all pledged, promised and bullied ourselves to eat better and exercise more, but so many times even the best intentions fall short', Dr Mike says. 'I incorporate healthy habits into my work and home life, and you can too.'

Do You Ever Wish You Could . . .

. . . Lose weight rapidly?

. . . Drop a dress size or two within a matter of weeks?

. . . Stay motivated on a diet and not get bored?

. . . Be more energetic and not so tired all the time?

. . . Feel better about yourself and your appearance almost right away?

. . . Not look and feel so bloated?

. . . Exercise less and still lose weight?

. . . Have people come up to you and ask you what diet you're on to look that wonderful?

. . . See high levels of the 'bad' LDL cholesterol, blood pressure and blood sugar start to drop?

. . . Stay at your goal weight with no more going up and down?

. . . Enjoy yourself on weekends and not have to watch every morsel you put in your mouth?

If you answered yes to any of these questions,
The 17 Day Diet and *The 17 Day Diet Workbook* are for you!

The 17 Day Diet Workbook

Your Guide to Healthy Weight Loss with Rapid Results

DR MIKE MORENO

**SIMON &
SCHUSTER**

London · New York · Sydney · Toronto · New Delhi

A CBS COMPANY

First published in Great Britain in 2011 by Simon & Schuster UK Ltd
A CBS COMPANY

1 3 5 7 9 10 8 6 4 2

Simon & Schuster UK Ltd
1st Floor
222 Gray's Inn Road
London
WC1X 8HB

www.simonandschuster.co.uk

Simon & Schuster Australia, Sydney
Simon & Schuster India, New Delhi

A CIP catalogue copy for this book
is available from the British Library.

ISBN: 978-0-85720-939-9

Printed in the UK by CPI Mackays, Chatham ME5 8TD

Contents

Get Started

· · · · · · · · · · · · · ·

Welcome to *The 17 Day Diet Workbook* – a practical, easy-to-use guide that supports *The 17 Day Diet*. The 17 Day Diet is a four-cycle programme designed to take weight off *rapidly*. Isn't that what we all want? Absolutely – hardly anyone I know, or any of my patients, likes to *endure* depressingly slow weight loss. We want to be trim now . . . look great now . . . and feel great now. That's what the 17 Day Diet does – gets you to where you want to be quickly, without a lot of sacrifice, hunger pangs or cravings. The diet is nutritionally sound too, easy to follow and it works. I call it the best thing since the sliced bread you'll give up (but only for the first two cycles).

How Fast Can I Lose Weight?
· ·

I've seen people lose up to 4.5 to 5.4 kg (10 to 12 pounds) in the first 17 days, and keep losing steadily right down to their goals. The beauty of this programme is that you won't get discouraged or bored by the prospect of staying on a diet for what seems like for ever – because you're shedding fat so quickly. You'll love the fact that in seven, ten or 17 days, you'll be slimmer. And if your results are like so many others, you'll feel a lot lighter and have an absurd amount of energy.

The 17 Day Diet really is simple and effective. Of course you'll keep a few 'forbidden foods' off your plate for the first three cycles, but feel free to enjoy all the rest.

What Is Forbidden?

Forbidden isn't really the right word, because nothing is off limits after the first three cycles. But the foods you will ban temporarily – and later reintroduce only sparingly – are the foods like bread, pasta and anything made with flour.

You'll also want to become a stranger to sugary fizzy drinks, fruit juices and drinks, jams, jellies, baked goods and many desserts.

How Is the Diet Structured?

The beauty of the 17 Day Diet is that it works in four cycles, depending on how much weight you'd like to lose.

Cycle 1 is the initial 17-day period in which you give up all bread, rice, potatoes, pasta, baked goods, fruits, sweets, cake, ice cream and alcohol. It's the strictest period, but also when the most rapid weight loss occurs. And it's easier than you think. You won't even miss carbs after a few days – your body gets used to not relying on them. You get to eat unlimited amounts of certain proteins and vegetables. And you'll supplement your daily diet with probiotics like yoghurt and kefir – foods shown in research to help the body burn fat.

The great thing about Cycle 1 is that you can use it anytime: when you need to break a plateau, get back to your goal weight, fit into a smaller dress size for the weekend or a swimming costume for a cruise – any time you want to accelerate your weight loss and do it safely. Cycle 1 is one of your best quick-weight loss resources.

During Cycle 2 you slowly begin to reintroduce certain carbs back into the diet, such as pulses, wholegrains and starchy vegetables, along with lots of other foods. Weight loss continues, and still fairly rapidly. And now you can drink a little wine – something most diets forbid.

On Cycle 3 you get to eat a huge of array of healthy foods: breads, more meats, more starches and fun foods like low-carb frozen dessert treats. You ease off some of the strictness of the first two cycles whilst still continuing to knock off pounds. Every 17 days you're changing things so that you never get bored. Every day is exciting, because you see the results on your scale or in your looser-fitting clothes.

Cycle 4 is the maintenance period that, ideally, you stay on the rest of your life. It lets you stay at your new weight as long as you do two things: enjoy yourself on the weekend, and use your favourite cycle during the week. So once you're happy with your new svelte self, continue to enjoy occasional forbidden foods. Just do so carefully or you'll find yourself back on a slippery slope to your pre-diet pudgy self. If you fall off the wagon for a weekend or, say, on a holiday, don't panic. Just go back to Cycle 1 to quickly shave off any weight you gain.

You Mean I Can Cheat?

Yes, on the weekends, if you want to! If you stay on your favourite cycle during the week – that's when it's easiest to 'diet' – you can stray off track a bit on the weekends. Come Monday morning, you simply minimise any damage by getting back on one of the cycles.

Why Does the 17 Day Diet Work So Well?

Scientifically, eliminating unhealthy foods from your system keeps them from making a beeline to your belly and elsewhere. Healthy foods do the opposite. The higher amounts of lean protein you eat, for example, boost your metabolism in a number of physiologically active ways. This diet is high in fibre too. Fibre is an appetite suppressant, a detoxifier and a food component that ushers bad calories out of your system before they have time to camp out on your thighs. Then there is the addition of probiotics, now believed to keep fat formation in check.

Another reason the 17 Day Diet works is because you're changing your calorie count and the foods you eat. By varying these things, you keep your body and metabolism guessing. I call this 'body confusion'. The scale is less likely to get stuck. The added bonus: you'll never get bored. And it's fun watching those pounds melt off. So confusion is good!

But, more importantly, the 17 Day Diet works because it's realistic. Nothing derails a diet faster than distressing round-the-clock hunger pangs, or boredom. But the 17 Day Diet isn't about depriving yourself of food or variety. I encourage you to eat until you are no longer hungry – and even snack between meals – as long as you're eating the right foods. That doesn't mean just broccoli, either. Nuts, cheeses and other delicious foods are permitted as you progress through the cycles. There are so many choices too, that you'll never get bored on this plan.

OK, Let's Cut to the Chase!

You've read this and you're a believer, yet you can't wait to get started. To learn all the intricacies of how and why the diet works, you really need to get the book, *The 17 Day Diet*. But if you can't get to the bookshop straight away, here's an overview:

Quick and Easy Overview of the 17 Day Diet	
Cycles	**Purpose**
Cycle 1: Accelerate (17 days)	To promote rapid weight loss by improving digestive health. It helps clear sugar from the blood to boost fat-burning and discourage fat storage.
Cycle 2: Activate (17 days)	To reset your metabolism through a strategy that involves increasing and decreasing your caloric consumption to stimulate fat-burning and to help prevent plateaus.
Cycle 3: Achieve (17 days)	To develop good eating habits through the re-introduction of additional foods and move you closer to your goal weight.
Cycle 4: Arrive (ongoing)	To keep you at your goal weight through a programme of eating that lets you enjoy your favourite foods on weekends whilst eating healthily during the week.

Using This Journal

For losing weight on the 17 Day Diet, this journal is indispensable. You'll use it to keep track of your eating, exercise, strategies, goals and milestones – all motivational information. Once you start writing things down, you'll see patterns that start to emerge, you'll overcome obstacles to weight loss and you'll feel empowered to make positive changes in your life and your health.

I've made all of this simple for you with pages on which you can record information, quickly and easily. Part of the format includes simple checklists designed to save time.

Once you get the hang of keeping a journal, you'll love it – and the motivation it gives you to be your best ever.

Here's a summary of the practical tools you'll find in *The 17 Day Diet Workbook*:

Get Motivated

Start the journal and the 17 Day Diet by recording your motivations to lose weight. The more motivated you feel, the more success you'll have. Revisit this page often, especially if you need a nudge to keep going.

Your Starting Point and Goal Weight

You'll enter your starting weight and post pictures of yourself here. Then I'll help you find a realistic goal for your body type.

Daily Meal Planner

Yes, you must write down everything you eat, even if it's not on the diet. Then you can look back and say, 'Wow, I ate six cream-filled doughnuts on Tuesday. No wonder I'm not losing weight.'

I want you to be brutally honest and accountable to yourself. If you're going to fudge the truth about fudge, why even bother to keep a journal packed with fibs?

Here are some examples of *honest* entries:

> *Entry 1: Breakfast: yoghurt and an apple. Note: I wanted to reach for a big chocolate chip biscuit, but that would be like having whisky at 9 a.m. Deviant behaviour successfully avoided.*
>
> *Entry 2: Horrible day! At midnight I ate a packet of biscuits with two bowls of ice cream. Let's go for total failure.*

Seriously, you're less likely to have entries like that last one if you make keeping a journal a regular practice. You'll think twice about eating something bad if you have to put it down on paper. Writing down what you eat each day practically guarantees weight-loss success. In fact, dieters who record daily what they eat drop twice as much weight as those who don't, according to research. No one will read your journal but you – so at least try keeping a journal for the first 17 days and see if your eating habits improve.

Daily Exercise Planner

Whilst following the 17 Day Diet, plan on moving your body more (trips to the fridge don't count). I've included an exercise log on which you will record strength-training and cardio workouts. Please use this to:

- Plan out your workouts (in other words, write out each workout at least a day in advance.) Planning always leads to personal accountability.

- Fill in the spaces that ask you for progress benchmarks such as duration, calories burnt, poundages lifted and so forth.

- Analyse your logs at least once a week. Note where you've improved: you're lifting heavier weights, jogging further or pushing yourself to work out longer than 17 minutes. Seeing your progress on paper is incredibly motivating.

Reflection

Along the way I'll ask you a series of probing questions. Don't worry: they're for your eyes only, and there will not be a test. Write down what's working and what's not working. What did you do well? Where do you need to improve? These sections help you stay on track and change nonproductive habits.

Review

After each cycle you'll assess your success and prepare for your transition to the next cycle of the 17 Day Diet. I'll also ask you to consider any strategies for change.

Also in *The 17 Day Diet Workbook*:

Recipes

I've got 17 brand new, mouth-watering recipes for you to help guide your menu decisions. They take less than 30 minutes to whip together, and are geared for the four cycles of this programme.

Shopping List

This features an expanded list of foods and shows you how to shop for weight-loss success. Each food is matched to its appropriate cycle.

Food Guide

We don't count calories or nutrients on the 17 Day Diet per se, but this mini food guide gives you important nutritional information on the foods you'll be eating.

Exercise Guide

Since exercise burns calories, this section shows you how many calories are burnt per hour in any number of activities, from attending an aerobic dance class to pulling weeds in your garden. Consult this chart to see how many calories you're burning through exercise, then record that number in your exercise planner.

Tips

Every day I'll give a tip to help you stay on track. To use this journal successfully let me start with a few basic tips now:

1. Correctly follow the 17 Day Diet instructions.
2. Purchase *The 17 Day Diet* book.
3. Take before, after and during photos.
4. Use and fill in this journal daily.

Along the way I'll show you how to critically analyse what your journal reveals. This is so important, since most of us live on the surface, never touching any depth. Many people are just too busy to listen to the world inside them and spend too much time listening to the world outside them. To keep a journal takes silence, reflection and slowing down.

Now for a few specifics to get you started on the right track. . . .

Get Motivated

· · · · · · · · · · · · · · · · · ·

I'm sure you have many reasons why you want to lose weight, but the most important one is you and your quality of life. In the space below write down all the reasons (including that one!) and motivations for losing weight – and keeping it off. Revisit your writings here at least once a week, or whenever you feel your motivation waning.

My Motivation

Why Losing Weight Matters to Me

My Motivation

Why Losing Weight Matters to Me

My Motivation

Why Losing Weight Matters to Me

My Motivation

Why Losing Weight Matters to Me

Your Starting Point and Goal Weight

••

You can't get anywhere if you don't know where you're going. I'm sure your goal is to drop approximately a whole lot of weight, preferably in the form of fat, but water will do as long as it brings results on the scale. The key is to set a realistic and attainable weight for your frame. With an appropriate goal ahead of you, you're much more likely to continue – and even look forward to – your plan. Goal setting improves the possibility of success and boosts positive psychological changes in self-confidence and motivation.

How Much Should You Weigh?
•••••••••••••••••••••••••••••••••••••••

As you begin the 17 Day Diet, select a specific weight goal – a weight at which you feel you will look your best. Keep in mind that there's really no such thing as the 'perfect' weight because we all come in variety of body shapes, heights and bone structures. However, there are ideal weight ranges, so there is a simple equation I tend to follow:

If you're a woman: Start with 45.4 kg (100 lb) for the first 152.5 cm (5 ft)of your height, and add 2.5 kg (5 lb) for each extra 2.5 cm (1 in) to get the midpoint of what your ideal body weight range should be. Then you need to factor in your body structure. Some people are smaller boned, others are big boned. If you're small boned, I subtract 15 per cent from the normal frame weights; if you're large boned, I add 15 per cent to the normal frame weights. For a lot of people that's too much maths. So I did the maths for you:

WOMEN		
Small-Boned Frame	*Midpoint*	*Large-Boned Frame*
152.5 cm = 38.5 kg	**152.5 cm = 54.4 kg**	152.5 cm = 52.2 kg
155 cm = 41 kg	**155 cm = 47.6 kg**	155 cm = 54.9 kg
157.5 cm = 42.6 kg	**157.5 cm = 49.9 kg**	157.5 cm = 57.6 kg
160 cm = 44.5 kg	**160 cm = 52.2 kg**	160 cm = 59.9 kg
162.5 cm = 46.3 kg	**162.5 cm = 54.4 kg**	162.5 cm = 621 kg
165 cm = 48 kg	**165 cm = 57.7 kg**	165 cm = 65.3 kg
167.5 cm = 49.9 kg	**167.5 cm = 59 kg**	167.5 cm = 68 kg
170 cm = 52.2 kg	**170 cm = 61.2 kg**	170 cm = 70.3 kg
172.5 cm = 54 kg	**172.5 cm = 63.5 kg**	172.5 cm = 73 kg
175 cm = 55.8 kg	**175 cm = 65.8 kg**	175 cm = 75.4 kg
177.5 cm = 58 kg	**177.5 cm = 68 kg**	177.5 cm = 78.5 kg
180 cm = 59.9 kg	**180 cm = 70.8 kg**	180 cm = 80.7 kg
182.5 cm = 61.7 kg	**182.5 cm = 72.6 kg**	182.5 cm = 83.5 kg

Need to convert from imperial? If you know your height in feet and inches, multiply the feet by 12 – remember from your old school days there are 12 inches to a foot – and add to the inches, then multiply that figure by 2.54 to get centimetres. So, if you are 5 ft 4 in, 5 x 12 = 60 + 4 = 64, then 64 x 2.54 = 162.5 cm (or almost, 162.56 cm to be exact). For weight, 1 pound = 0.4535 kilograms, so if you weigh 10 stone 3 lb (remember, 14 lb to a stone), 10 x 14 = 140 + 3 = 143 lb, then 143 x 0.4535 = 64.85 kg.

If you're a man: Take 49.9 kg (110 lb) for the first 152.5 cm (5 ft) of your height and add 2.7 kg (6 lb) for each extra 2.5 cm (1 in) to get the midpoint of what should be your ideal body weight range. Allow for being small or large boned, as explained above.

A caveat: These charts are only rough estimates with a large range of variability. We are all made differently, and there is not one ideal weight for every height. Base your goal on a weight at which you feel and look your best – a goal also approved by your doctor.

MEN		
Small-Boned Frame	*Midpoint*	*Large-Boned Frame*
152.5 cm = 42.6 kg	**152.5 cm = 49.9 kg**	152.5 cm = 57.6 kg
155 cm = 44.9 kg	**155 cm = 52.6 kg**	155 cm = 60.3 kg
157.5 cm = 47.2 kg	**157.5 cm = 53.5 kg**	157.5 cm = 63.5 kg
160 cm = 49.4 kg	**160 cm = 58 kg**	160 cm = 66.7 kg
162.5 cm = 51.7 kg	**162.5 cm = 60.8 kg**	162.5 cm = 69.9 kg
165 cm = 54 kg	**165 cm = 63.5 kg**	165 cm = 73 kg
167.5 cm = 56.2 kg	**167.5 cm = 66.2 kg**	167.5 cm = 76.2 kg
170 cm = 58.5 kg	**170 cm = 68.9 kg**	170 cm = 79.4 kg
172.5 cm = 60.8 kg	**172.5 cm = 71.7 kg**	172.5 cm = 82.6 kg
175 cm = 63 kg	**175 cm = 74.4 kg**	175 cm = 85.7 kg
177.5 cm = 65.8 kg	**177.5 cm = 77.1 kg**	177.5 cm = 88.9 kg
180 cm = 68 kg	**180 cm = 79.8 kg**	180 cm = 91.6 kg
183 cm = 70.3 kg	**183 cm = 82.6 kg**	183 cm = 94.8 kg
185.5 cm = 72.6 kg	**185.5 cm = 85.3 kg**	185.5 cm = 98 kg
188 cm = 74.8 kg	**188 cm = 88 kg**	188 cm = 101.2 kg
190.5 cm = 77.1 kg	**190.5 cm = 90.7 kg**	190.5 cm = 104.3 kg
193 cm = 79.4 kg	**193 cm = 93.4 kg**	193 cm = 107.5 kg
195.5 cm = 81.4 kg	**195.5 cm = 96.2 kg**	195.5 cm = 110.7 kg
198 cm = 83.9 kg	**198 cm = 98.9 kg**	198 cm = 113.9 kg

Write It Down!

I've always been a goal setter. I love the idea of writing down what I want to achieve and then watching my life improve as I make the changes to make that goal a reality. I've never accomplished a goal without significant benefits to my life in ways I didn't anticipate. (However, there is a downside to being a goal setter. When the goal is achieved, I feel a little adrift. I end up having a significant discussion with myself about what's next and why.) Anyway, in the space below please write down your goal weight (and expect to achieve it!)

My Starting Weight	Be sure to weigh yourself on the morning you start the 17 Day Diet. Record your weight in the box at the left.
My Goal Weight	Using the charts above, select a goal weight. Enter it in the box at the left. I'll ask you to monitor your progress towards your goal all the way through the 17 Day Diet.

Let Me Ask You . . .

About your weight goals, I'd like you to consider some of the issues below before you get started. Then write out your answers.

1. **Your desired weight:**

   Why do you want to be at this weight?

   _____

   _____

   _____

   _____

   _____

   What is special about this weight?

   _____

   _____

   _____

   _____

   _____

2. **Past weight goals:**

   Have you set weight goals in the past?

   _____

   _____

   _____

   _____

   _____

Were they different from this goal? If yes, why?

_____

_____

_____

_____

_____

3. **Your weight history:**

When were you last at your desired weight?

_____

_____

_____

_____

_____

What could keep you from staying at that weight?

_____

_____

_____

_____

_____

How would you avoid those obstacles?

_____

_____

_____

_____

_____

4. **Getting to your goal:**

How important is it to get to your goal?

_____

_____

_____

_____

_____

If it is important, why?

_____

_____

_____

_____

_____

5. **Not getting to your goal:**

How would you feel if you didn't reach your desired goal?

_____

_____

_____

_____

_____

What effect would it have on your self-confidence, health and fitness, social life, personal relationships and other aspects of daily life?

_____

_____

_____

_____

_____

Really think about your answers. What you write can often hold solutions to achieving what you desire in life. Come back to this part of the journal if you ever find yourself slipping.

Visual Motivation: Take Before and After Photos

Take a picture of yourself before you start the 17 Day Diet. Follow up by taking pictures after every cycle in the same outfit, whether a swimming costume or work-out clothing, and then compare. You may not realise the changes your body is making on a daily basis, but the photographs can put things into perspective. Finally take an 'After' photo when you reach your goal.

Paste your photos in the spaces below.

Before

After Cycle 1

After Cycle 2

After Cycle 3

After Cycle 4 or at Your Goal Weight

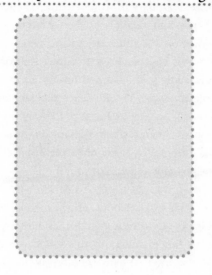

Incentives

Whenever possible create incentives to help you reach your goals. For example, if you want to lose weight, buy an expensive outfit that's several sizes too small. The thought of having a beautiful outfit unused in your wardrobe can be an effective impetus to keep you going. Or hang it up on your door so you can see it every day. On a weekly basis try it on and see how it fits. If you can barely fit into it, wait and then try it on again later. Alternatively, suggest to your spouse or partner that you be taken on a romantic holiday if you reach your self-determined goal. Getting others involved in your weight loss effort builds a support network that can spur you on to greater heights.

Visualise Your Success

Visualisation is a technique that can be used to reinforce goals and sustain your motivation. Essentially it is an organised form of daydreaming. Many athletes use this technique to actualise their potential. A netball player, for instance, might visualise swishing a last-second jump shot or a cricket batsman might visualise hitting a ball clear over the boundary to score six runs. The technique works beautifully in fitness and weight loss, where it has been demonstrated to increase motivation and adherence to a programme.

This approach is best practised in a quiet environment without any distractions. Close your eyes and relax your muscles. Begin to think about your physique. Visualise each problem area – abs, bum, thighs and so forth – and get an image of the way you want them to look. Picture yourself in great shape, walking on the beach in a bikini or wearing a sexy dress at an event. Make the image as clear and realistic as possible, seeing it as a film in your head.

You might even want to think of a person whose physique you admire such as a famous celebrity, fitness model or perhaps even someone who works out in your gym. Fantasise that you possess the body of your role model and carry this vision with you. Let your imagination be your internal source of motivation.

This journal is designed to make losing weight on the 17 Day Diet more personal, more fun, motivating and ultimately, more successful. What you learn about yourself over the four cycles of this programme can carry over into a lifetime of good health and a healthy weight. You've got all it takes. It's all right here, and within you. Now . . . here's an amazing four-cycle plan to help you get lean, fit, strong and motivated.

CYCLE 1

. . . .

Accelerate

GOAL:

To trigger rapid weight loss in a healthy manner by mobilising fat stores and flushing water and toxins from your system.

What to Eat: The Accelerate Cycle Food List

Lean Proteins

Here's where you'll be getting a lot of your fat-burning power. Eat all you want of the following proteins. They're freebies. The 17 Day Diet is purposely high in protein because protein stimulates the reduction of body fat.

Fish*

Canned light tuna *(in water)*

Catfish

Plaice

Haddock

Halibut

Herring

Perch *(ocean)*

Salmon, canned or fresh

Sardines *(canned in mustard or tomato sauce, not oil)*

Sole

Tilapia

Trout *(freshwater)*

Tuna

---

*See the Food Guide on pages 301–304 for other fish allowed in Cycle 1. Opt for wild-caught rather than farm-raised fish, which may have received doses of antibiotics. However, avoid shark and swordfish. They are the most likely to carry metals like methylmercury, which is considered a toxin.

Poultry

   Chicken breasts
   Turkey breasts
   Mince turkey, lean
   Eggs *(2 eggs = 1 serving)*
   Egg whites *(4 egg whites = 1 serving)*

Cleansing Vegetables

Eat all you want from the following list. They're freebies too. I call
these 'cleansing vegetables' because they support detoxification in
the intestines, blood and liver, and offer protective antioxidants.

   Artichoke
   Artichoke hearts
   Asparagus
   Aubergines
   Broccoli
   Brussels sprouts
   Cabbage
   Carrots
   Cauliflower
   Celery
   Cucumbers
   French beans
   Garlic
   Green, leafy vegetables *(including beetroot greens, spring greens,*
        turnip greens)
   Kale
   Leeks
   Lettuces, all varieties
   Mushrooms
   Okra
   Onions
   Parsley
   Salad onions

Spinach
Sweet peppers: green, orange, red, yellow
Tomatoes
Watercress

Low-Sugar Fruit – 2 servings daily

Low-sugar fruits are good sources of fibre, which provides bulk and digests slowly, helping you feel full. They're also full of water and super low in calories, which makes them ideal for weight loss.

Apples
Berries, all types
Grapefruit
Oranges
Peaches
Pears
Plums
Prunes
Red grapes

Probiotic Foods – 2 servings daily

Probiotics help balance your digestive system, resulting in an overall increase in the efficiency of digestion. Research shows that probiotics may also help fight obesity. There's no recommended daily allowance for probiotics. To maintain health, 5–10 billion is adequate. That may sound like a lot, but consider this: a 175-g/6-oz serving of yoghurt contains around 17 billion probiotics.

Yoghurt, any type, including Greek-style, sugar-free fruit
flavoured, natural and low-fat *(175-g/6-oz container = 1 serving)*
Kefir: similar to a drinking-style yoghurt; great for making
smoothies *(240 ml/8 fl oz = 1 serving)*
Low-fat acidophilus milk *(240 ml/8 fl oz = 1 serving)*
Yakult *(1 small 50-calorie bottle = 1 serving)*

Reduced salt miso dissolved in low-fat, low-sodium broth
(1 tablespoon = 1 serving)
Tempeh: a fermented cake of pressed soya beans *(115 g/4 oz = 1 serving)*
Sauerkraut *(115 g/4 oz = 1 serving)*
Kimchi: Korean cabbage; find it in Oriental supermarkets and enjoy
a small amount as a side dish with meals *(45 g/1½ oz = 1 serving)*

Friendly Fats: 1 to 2 tablespoons daily

Olive oil
Linseed oil

Condiments

Condiments and seasonings are allowed in moderation: salsa, low-carb pasta sauce, light soy sauce, reduced-sugar tomato ketchup, fat-free soured cream, low-fat, low-sodium broth, a natural low-calorie sweetener, sugar-free jams and jellies, vegetable cooking spray, fat-free cheeses (i.e. Parmesan), fat-free salad dressing, salt, pepper, vinegar, mustard, herbs and spices.

Meal Planning Made Easy

It's easy to remember what to eat during this cycle:

- As much as you want of specific proteins and cleansing vegetables.
- Supplement these foods with 2 low-sugar fruits daily, 2 servings of probiotic foods such as yoghurt, kefir, Yakult, acidophilus milk, reduced salt miso dissolved in low-fat, low-sodium broth or sauerkraut (115 g/4 oz a serving), and 1 to 2 tablespoons of friendly fat. It's that easy.

You do not have to count anything, except your 2 fruit daily servings, your 2 daily probiotic servings and your fat serving.
Here is a sample menu on the Accelerate Cycle.

Wake-up drink

Every morning, as soon as you rise, drink one 240-ml/8-fl-oz cup of hot water. Squeeze half a lemon into the cup; the lemon stimulates your digestive juices. Your goal is to drink at least seven more glasses of water by the end of the day.

Day 1

Breakfast

- 2 scrambled egg whites
- ½ grapefruit, or other fresh fruit
- 1 cup green tea

Lunch

- Large green salad topped with tuna; drizzle with 1 tablespoon of olive or linseed oil and 2 tablespoons balsamic vinegar
- 1 cup green tea

Dinner

- Plenty of grilled chicken with liberal amounts of any vegetables from the list, steamed or raw.
- 1 cup green tea

Snacks

- 175 g/6 oz of sugar-free natural yoghurt mixed with 1–2 table-spoons sugar-free jam; or other probiotic serving.
- 1 serving of fruit from the list

DAY 1 – MY DAILY FOOD CHART   DATE

Dr Mike's Food Tip of the Day

Start thinking like a weight-loss winner. To be successful you have to overcome the self-defeating thoughts that plague people trying to lose weight. Don't set unrealistic goals you can't control. Be positive about what you can do. If you slip, ignore it and continue with your programme. Find the hidden triggers that cause you problems, and avoid these triggers.

WEIGHT

WATER INTAKE

number of 240-ml/
8-fl-oz glasses

☐ ☐ ☐ ☐
☐ ☐ ☐ ☐

FOOD INTAKE

number of servings

☐ Lean Proteins

☐ Cleansing
Vegetables

☐ Low Sugar Fruit
(2 servings)

☐ Probiotic Foods
(2 servings)

☐ Friendly Fats
(1–2 tablespoons)

Breakfast

_____
_____
_____
_____
_____

Lunch

_____
_____
_____
_____

Dinner

_____
_____
_____
_____

Snacks

_____
_____
_____

Dr Mike's Workout Tip of the Day

Exercising at lower levels of exertion encourages the body to burn fat, so go easy on yourself! It's Day 1 of Cycle 1, so all you need to do is get in 17 minutes of easy exercising today, like walking around your neighbourhood or inside a nearby shopping centre.

Cardio

TIME	ACTIVITY DESCRIPTION	DURATION	CALORIES BURNT	DISTANCE	STEPS

Toning Exercises

EXERCISES	SETS	REPS	WEIGHT	TIME	CALORIES BURNT

DAY 1	MY DAILY JOURNAL

What worked well?

_____

_____

_____

What didn't work well?

_____

_____

_____

I experienced the following changes:

_____

_____

_____

**Ways to overcome these challenges
(brainstorm as many problem solvers as you can):**

_____

_____

_____

**From your list choose the best solutions and develop
strategies for success.**

_____

_____

_____

Reflections: Write in your journal how you're feeling, your successes,
anything that comes to mind about your progress so far. Read through
The 17 Day Diet book to learn about all my strategies for overcoming
barriers. Which ones can you apply today?

_____

_____

_____

_____

_____

_____

DAY 2 – MY DAILY FOOD CHART   DATE

Dr Mike's Food Tip of the Day

Leaner, stronger, healthier – that's what eating vegetables will do for your body! Dieters who eat the widest variety of veggies have the least amount of body fat, according to a Tufts University study in the US. So get thin, not flabby. Eat as many of the cleansing vegetables as you want during Cycle 1 of the 17 Day Diet.

WEIGHT

WATER INTAKE

number of 240-ml/
8-fl-oz glasses

☐ ☐ ☐ ☐
☐ ☐ ☐ ☐

FOOD INTAKE

number of servings

☐ Lean Proteins

☐ Cleansing
   Vegetables

☐ Low Sugar Fruit
   (2 servings)

☐ Probiotic Foods
   (2 servings)

☐ Friendly Fats
   (1–2 tablespoons)

Breakfast

_____
_____
_____
_____
_____
_____

Lunch

_____
_____
_____
_____

Dinner

_____
_____
_____
_____

Snacks

_____
_____
_____

Dr Mike's Workout Tip of the Day

As you complete your 17-minute workout today, visualise the new you – the 'you' with the trained, toned physique who is active, healthy and enjoying life. Keep this picture in your mind as you make it happen, day by day.

Cardio

TIME	ACTIVITY DESCRIPTION	DURATION	CALORIES BURNT	DISTANCE	STEPS

Toning Exercises

EXERCISES	SETS	REPS	WEIGHT	TIME	CALORIES BURNT

DAY 2 – MY DAILY JOURNAL

What worked well?

_____

_____

_____

What didn't work well?

_____

_____

_____

I experienced the following changes:

_____

_____

_____

Ways to overcome these challenges
(brainstorm as many problem solvers as you can):

_____

_____

_____

From your list choose the best solutions and develop
strategies for success.

_____

_____

_____

Reflections: Write in your journal how you're feeling, your successes,
anything that comes to mind about your progress so far. Read through
The 17 Day Diet book to learn about all my strategies for overcoming
barriers. Which ones can you apply today?

_____

_____

_____

_____

_____

_____

DAY 3 – MY DAILY FOOD CHART   DATE

Dr Mike's Food Tip of the Day

Fruit is good for you, right? Yes, it is, but certain fruits like pineapple, watermelon and bananas are high in sugar and do not promote fat loss. So choose low sugar fruits – berries, apples, oranges and grapefruit – throughout Cycle 1. Only two servings a day, please, and consume them before 2 p.m. Fruit is a carb and timing of carbohydrate intake is important!

WEIGHT

WATER INTAKE

number of 240-ml/
8-fl-oz glasses

☐ ☐ ☐ ☐
☐ ☐ ☐ ☐

FOOD INTAKE

number of servings

☐ Lean Proteins

☐ Cleansing
Vegetables

☐ Low Sugar Fruit
(2 servings)

☐ Probiotic Foods
(2 servings)

☐ Friendly Fats
(1–2 tablespoons)

Breakfast

_____
_____
_____
_____
_____

Lunch

_____
_____
_____
_____

Dinner

_____
_____
_____
_____

Snacks

_____
_____
_____

Dr Mike's Workout Tip of the Day

Think of your 17-minute workout not as 'work' but as 17 minutes of moving your body and doing something you enjoy. Are you a fan of one of the dance shows on TV, like *Strictly Come Dancing* or *So You Think You Can Dance?* Do *you* like to dance? Put on your favourite music and move!

Cardio

TIME	ACTIVITY DESCRIPTION	DURATION	CALORIES BURNT	DISTANCE	STEPS

Toning Exercises

EXERCISES	SETS	REPS	WEIGHT	TIME	CALORIES BURNT

DAY 3 – MY DAILY JOURNAL

What worked well?

_____
_____
_____

What didn't work well?

_____
_____
_____

I experienced the following changes:

_____
_____
_____

**Ways to overcome these challenges
(brainstorm as many problem solvers as you can):**

_____
_____
_____

**From your list choose the best solutions and develop
strategies for success.**

_____
_____
_____

Reflections: Write in your journal how you're feeling, your successes,
anything that comes to mind about your progress so far. Read through
The 17 Day Diet book to learn about all my strategies for overcoming
barriers. Which ones can you apply today?

_____
_____
_____
_____
_____
_____

DAY 4 – MY DAILY FOOD CHART   DATE

Dr Mike's Food Tip of the Day

As I explained in *The 17 Day Diet* book, bugs can be good for you! Good 'bugs' or bacteria help your digestive tract form a barrier against bad bacteria. That's why I suggest two servings a day of the friendly type of bacteria called probiotics. Found in yoghurt, kefir, miso, tempeh and others, these good guys also help you lose weight!

WEIGHT

WATER INTAKE

number of 240-ml/
8-fl-oz glasses

☐ ☐ ☐ ☐
☐ ☐ ☐ ☐

FOOD INTAKE

number of servings

☐ Lean Proteins

☐ Cleansing
   Vegetables

☐ Low Sugar Fruit
   (2 servings)

☐ Probiotic Foods
   (2 servings)

☐ Friendly Fats
   (1–2 tablespoons)

Breakfast

_____
_____
_____
_____
_____
_____

Lunch

_____
_____
_____
_____

Dinner

_____
_____
_____
_____

Snacks

_____
_____
_____

Dr Mike's Workout Tip of the Day

If you're working out on your own, put your gym times on your daily calendar. And think about getting your workouts in early. I have found that people who get up in the morning and exercise the first thing tend to stay with programmes longer. They get it over with and feel so much better the rest of the day.

Cardio

TIME	ACTIVITY DESCRIPTION	DURATION	CALORIES BURNT	DISTANCE	STEPS

Toning Exercises

EXERCISES	SETS	REPS	WEIGHT	TIME	CALORIES BURNT

DAY 4 – MY DAILY JOURNAL

What worked well?

_____

_____

_____

What didn't work well?

_____

_____

_____

I experienced the following changes:

_____

_____

_____

Ways to overcome these challenges
(brainstorm as many problem solvers as you can):

_____

_____

_____

From your list choose the best solutions and develop
strategies for success.

_____

_____

_____

Reflections: Write in your journal how you're feeling, your successes, anything that comes to mind about your progress so far. Read through *The 17 Day Diet* book to learn about all my strategies for overcoming barriers. Which ones can you apply today?

_____

_____

_____

_____

_____

_____

DAY 5 – MY DAILY FOOD CHART   DATE

Dr Mike's Food Tip of the Day

How many times have you been told that you should drink eight 240-ml/8-fl-oz glasses of water each day? A thousand times? Well, now you've been told a thousand and one times! And here's why: drinking water is essential to weight loss and helps your body metabolise stored fat. It also helps the body flush waste from your system and is the best solution for fluid retention.

WEIGHT

Breakfast

WATER INTAKE

number of 240-ml/
8-fl-oz glasses

☐ ☐ ☐ ☐
☐ ☐ ☐ ☐

FOOD INTAKE

number of servings

Lunch

☐ Lean Proteins

☐ Cleansing
Vegetables

☐ Low Sugar Fruit
(2 servings)

Dinner

☐ Probiotic Foods
(2 servings)

☐ Friendly Fats
(1–2 tablespoons)

Snacks

Dr Mike's Workout Tip of the Day

Have you recruited a workout buddy? The accountability your spouse, your children or a friend from work can provide can keep you going when you'd rather just collapse in the recliner. So, pair up with someone for your 17 minute workout whenever possible. It's a lot harder to talk yourself out of exercising when someone else is counting on you!

Cardio

TIME	ACTIVITY DESCRIPTION	DURATION	CALORIES BURNT	DISTANCE	STEPS

Toning Exercises

EXERCISES	SETS	REPS	WEIGHT	TIME	CALORIES BURNT

DAY 5 – MY DAILY JOURNAL

What worked well?

_____

_____

_____

What didn't work well?

_____

_____

_____

I experienced the following changes:

_____

_____

_____

Ways to overcome these challenges
(brainstorm as many problem solvers as you can):

_____

_____

_____

From your list choose the best solutions and develop
strategies for success.

_____

_____

_____

Reflections: Write in your journal how you're feeling, your successes,
anything that comes to mind about your progress so far. Read through
The 17 Day Diet book to learn about all my strategies for overcoming
barriers. Which ones can you apply today?

_____

_____

_____

_____

_____

_____

DAY 6 – MY DAILY FOOD CHART   DATE

Dr Mike's Food Tip of the Day

Whoops! Do I see you recording the cup of tea you had with lunch towards your daily water intake? Sorry, but coffee and tea do not count towards your eight glasses of water . . . neither do diet fizzy drinks, regular fizzy drinks, energy drinks, juice, sports drinks or flavoured waters, but feel free to add a lemon or lime wedge to good ol' H_2O.

WEIGHT

WATER INTAKE

number of 240-ml/
8-fl-oz glasses

☐ ☐ ☐ ☐
☐ ☐ ☐ ☐

FOOD INTAKE

number of servings

☐ Lean Proteins

☐ Cleansing
Vegetables

☐ Low Sugar Fruit
(2 servings)

☐ Probiotic Foods
(2 servings)

☐ Friendly Fats
(1–2 tablespoons)

Breakfast

_____

_____

_____

_____

_____

Lunch

_____

_____

_____

_____

Dinner

_____

_____

_____

Snacks

_____

_____

_____

Dr Mike's Workout Tip of the Day

Break it up! If 17 minutes at one time seems challenging at first, try breaking up your workout into two manageable parts. Maybe you can fit in a 10-minute walk over your lunch hour, then take a short (at least 7 minute) bicycle ride after dinner. Whatever it takes, get your body used to moving for a minimum of 17 minutes every day, without fail.

Cardio

TIME	ACTIVITY DESCRIPTION	DURATION	CALORIES BURNT	DISTANCE	STEPS

Toning Exercises

EXERCISES	SETS	REPS	WEIGHT	TIME	CALORIES BURNT

DAY 6 – MY DAILY JOURNAL

What worked well?

_____
_____
_____

What didn't work well?

_____
_____
_____

I experienced the following changes:

_____
_____
_____

**Ways to overcome these challenges
(brainstorm as many problem solvers as you can):**

_____
_____
_____

**From your list choose the best solutions and develop
strategies for success.**

_____
_____
_____

Reflections: Write in your journal how you're feeling, your successes,
anything that comes to mind about your progress so far. Read through
The 17 Day Diet book to learn about all my strategies for overcoming
barriers. Which ones can you apply today?

_____
_____
_____
_____
_____
_____

DAY 7 – MY DAILY FOOD CHART   DATE

Dr Mike's Food Tip of the Day

What's so special about green tea? Besides water, green tea is a drink
of choice, thanks to certain chemicals it contains that increase fat
burning and stimulate the calorie-burning process. New research sug-
gests that something in green tea inhibits a process of blood vessel
growth that can cause fat tissue to grow. In light of all this, drinking
three cups of green tea daily is highly recommended.

WEIGHT

WATER INTAKE

number of 240-ml/
8-fl-oz glasses

☐ ☐ ☐ ☐
☐ ☐ ☐ ☐

FOOD INTAKE

number of servings

☐ Lean Proteins

☐ Cleansing
Vegetables

☐ Low Sugar Fruit
(2 servings)

☐ Probiotic Foods
(2 servings)

☐ Friendly Fats
(1–2 tablespoons)

Breakfast

_____

_____

_____

_____

_____

Lunch

_____

_____

_____

_____

Dinner

_____

_____

_____

_____

Snacks

_____

_____

_____

Dr Mike's Workout Tip of the Day

Stretching your muscles for a minute or two before and after you walk or participate in any type of workout will help prevent injuries, limit soreness and improve flexibility. Warming up also helps ease your body into your workout by slowly increasing your heart rate and breathing. Cooling down is also important since stopping abruptly can cause dizziness, cramping or muscle soreness.

Cardio

TIME	ACTIVITY DESCRIPTION	DURATION	CALORIES BURNT	DISTANCE	STEPS

Toning Exercises

EXERCISES	SETS	REPS	WEIGHT	TIME	CALORIES BURNT

DAY 7 – MY DAILY JOURNAL

What worked well?

_____

_____

_____

What didn't work well?

_____

_____

_____

I experienced the following changes:

_____

_____

_____

Ways to overcome these challenges
(brainstorm as many problem solvers as you can):

_____

_____

_____

From your list choose the best solutions and develop
strategies for success.

_____

_____

_____

Reflections: Write in your journal how you're feeling, your successes,
anything that comes to mind about your progress so far. Read through
The 17 Day Diet book to learn about all my strategies for overcoming
barriers. Which ones can you apply today?

_____

_____

_____

_____

_____

_____

DAY 8 – MY DAILY FOOD CHART   DATE

Dr Mike's Food Tip of the Day

Fats can actually help you burn fat! Not all fats are bad guys, like the trans fats found in processed foods and the saturated fats found in animal products. Friendly fats are the polyunsaturated ones mostly found in fish and vegetable oils. Omega-3 fatty acids, for example, boost your metabolism. In Cycle 1 choose salmon or canned light tuna (in water). For cooking (1–2 tablespoons daily) choose olive oil or linseed oil.

WEIGHT

WATER INTAKE

number of 240-ml/
8-fl-oz glasses

☐ ☐ ☐ ☐
☐ ☐ ☐ ☐

FOOD INTAKE

number of servings

☐ Lean Proteins

☐ Cleansing
   Vegetables

☐ Low Sugar Fruit
   (2 servings)

☐ Probiotic Foods
   (2 servings)

☐ Friendly Fats
   (1–2 tablespoons)

Breakfast

_____
_____
_____
_____
_____

Lunch

_____
_____
_____
_____

Dinner

_____
_____
_____
_____

Snacks

_____
_____
_____

Dr Mike's Workout Tip of the Day

Stay safe whilst walking outdoors by wearing bright-coloured clothes and facing any approaching traffic. Riding a bicycle? The same defensive measures apply, plus a few more. Avoid potential injuries by wearing a helmet and making sure you can be seen by vehicles. Use a light and attach reflectors on your bicycle's wheels for added safety.

Cardio

TIME	ACTIVITY DESCRIPTION	DURATION	CALORIES BURNT	DISTANCE	STEPS

Toning Exercises

EXERCISES	SETS	REPS	WEIGHT	TIME	CALORIES BURNT

DAY 8 – MY DAILY JOURNAL

What worked well?

_____
_____
_____

What didn't work well?

_____
_____
_____

I experienced the following changes:

_____
_____
_____

Ways to overcome these challenges
(brainstorm as many problem solvers as you can):

_____
_____
_____

From your list choose the best solutions and develop
strategies for success.

_____
_____
_____

Reflections: Write in your journal how you're feeling, your successes, anything that comes to mind about your progress so far. Read through *The 17 Day Diet* book to learn about all my strategies for overcoming barriers. Which ones can you apply today?

_____
_____
_____
_____
_____
_____

DAY 9 – MY DAILY FOOD CHART   DATE

Dr Mike's Food Tip of the Day

Fresh or dried herbs and spices can add flavour and pizzazz to your meals. Basil and oregano can add an Italian flavour, whilst a sprinkling of cumin and chilli powder add a Mexican flair. Try a sprinkling of curry for an Indian taste or combine ginger with light soy sauce for an Oriental taste bud treat. Experiment! There is no reason for your meals to be bland and tasteless!

WEIGHT

WATER INTAKE

number of 240-ml/
8-fl-oz glasses

☐ ☐ ☐ ☐
☐ ☐ ☐ ☐

FOOD INTAKE

number of servings

☐ Lean Proteins

☐ Cleansing
Vegetables

☐ Low Sugar Fruit
(2 servings)

☐ Probiotic Foods
(2 servings)

☐ Friendly Fats
(1–2 tablespoons)

Breakfast

_____
_____
_____
_____
_____

Lunch

_____
_____
_____
_____

Dinner

_____
_____
_____
_____

Snacks

_____
_____
_____

Dr Mike's Workout Tip of the Day

Variety is the spice of life, and that also applies to your workout. Even if you really enjoy walking, change it up a couple days a week to keep things interesting. Try dusting off that badminton set in the garage and playing a few games after dinner with the children. Sign up for a ballroom dance class or a water aerobics session.

Cardio

TIME	ACTIVITY DESCRIPTION	DURATION	CALORIES BURNT	DISTANCE	STEPS

Toning Exercises

EXERCISES	SETS	REPS	WEIGHT	TIME	CALORIES BURNT

DAY 9 – MY DAILY JOURNAL

What worked well?

_____

_____

_____

What didn't work well?

_____

_____

_____

I experienced the following changes:

_____

_____

_____

Ways to overcome these challenges
(brainstorm as many problem solvers as you can):

_____

_____

_____

From your list choose the best solutions and develop
strategies for success.

_____

_____

_____

Reflections: Write in your journal how you're feeling, your successes,
anything that comes to mind about your progress so far. Read through
The 17 Day Diet book to learn about all my strategies for overcoming
barriers. Which ones can you apply today?

_____

_____

_____

_____

_____

_____

DAY 10 – MY DAILY FOOD CHART   DATE

Dr Mike's Food Tip of the Day

The more planning you do, the better off you are. Before you leave the house, grab a snack to take with you, like a piece of fruit, so you're not stopping at the takeaway instead. Stock up on healthy foods. No, Diet Coke and reduced-fat cakes don't count. Try new things, like raw spinach, new fruits, not stuffing yourself silly at buffets. Keep healthy snacks in your handbag, car and desk. Then hire bouncers to keep you away from all the spots where you hid all the unhealthy treats.

WEIGHT

WATER INTAKE

number of 240-ml/
8-fl-oz glasses

☐ ☐ ☐ ☐
☐ ☐ ☐ ☐

FOOD INTAKE

number of servings

☐ Lean Proteins

☐ Cleansing
  Vegetables

☐ Low Sugar Fruit
  (2 servings)

☐ Probiotic Foods
  (2 servings)

☐ Friendly Fats
  (1–2 tablespoons)

Breakfast

_____
_____
_____
_____
_____

Lunch

_____
_____
_____
_____

Dinner

_____
_____
_____
_____

Snacks

_____
_____
_____

Dr Mike's Workout Tip of the Day

Do you think of yourself as a good listener? If so, make sure you are listening to your body too! That means paying attention to sudden, sharp pains or prolonged fatigue. There is a difference between that 'good tired' feeling that follows a brisk walk and the kind of tired that lets you know you've overdone it. That's why I recommend taking things nice and easy during Cycle 1.

Cardio

TIME	ACTIVITY DESCRIPTION	DURATION	CALORIES BURNT	DISTANCE	STEPS

Toning Exercises

EXERCISES	SETS	REPS	WEIGHT	TIME	CALORIES BURNT

DAY 10 – MY DAILY JOURNAL

What worked well?

_____
_____
_____

What didn't work well?

_____
_____
_____

I experienced the following changes:

_____
_____
_____

**Ways to overcome these challenges
(brainstorm as many problem solvers as you can):**

_____
_____
_____

**From your list choose the best solutions and develop
strategies for success.**

_____
_____
_____

Reflections: Write in your journal how you're feeling, your successes,
anything that comes to mind about your progress so far. Read through
The 17 Day Diet book to learn about all my strategies for overcoming
barriers. Which ones can you apply today?

_____
_____
_____
_____
_____

DAY 11 – MY DAILY FOOD CHART   DATE

Dr Mike's Food Tip of the Day

Think you can't live without tomato ketchup or soured cream? Condiments, in moderation, may be incorporated into your Cycle 1 diet. Just choose the low-carb tomato ketchup, fat-free soured cream and sugar-free jams and jellies. Salsa, light soy sauce, fat-free salad dressings and cheeses, vinegar, mustard and vegetable cooking spray can also be on your shopping list. I also give a thumbs-up to using a noncaloric sweetener made from natural ingredients.

WEIGHT

WATER INTAKE

number of 240-ml/
8-fl-oz glasses

☐ ☐ ☐ ☐
☐ ☐ ☐ ☐

FOOD INTAKE

number of servings

☐ Lean Proteins

☐ Cleansing
Vegetables

☐ Low Sugar Fruit
(2 servings)

☐ Probiotic Foods
(2 servings)

☐ Friendly Fats
(1–2 tablespoons)

Breakfast

_____
_____
_____
_____
_____

Lunch

_____
_____
_____
_____

Dinner

_____
_____
_____
_____

Snacks

_____
_____
_____

Dr Mike's Workout Tip of the Day

Don't get discouraged! If you have been a couch potato for months or years, you can't expect to be ready to run a marathon in a week or two. However, by recording your workouts, you'll be able to track the progress you've made and soon will begin to feel it. Your energy level will increase, and you will slowly begin to feel stronger. There will be a lightness in your steps, because you will be shedding pounds too.

Cardio

TIME	ACTIVITY DESCRIPTION	DURATION	CALORIES BURNT	DISTANCE	STEPS

Toning Exercises

EXERCISES	SETS	REPS	WEIGHT	TIME	CALORIES BURNT

DAY 11 – MY DAILY JOURNAL

What worked well?

_____
_____
_____

What didn't work well?

_____
_____
_____

I experienced the following changes:

_____
_____
_____

**Ways to overcome these challenges
(brainstorm as many problem solvers as you can):**

_____
_____
_____

**From your list choose the best solutions and develop
strategies for success.**

_____
_____
_____

Reflections: Write in your journal how you're feeling, your successes,
anything that comes to mind about your progress so far. Read through
The 17 Day Diet book to learn about all my strategies for overcoming
barriers. Which ones can you apply today?

_____
_____
_____
_____
_____
_____

DAY 12 – MY DAILY FOOD CHART   DATE

Dr Mike's Food Tip of the Day

If you find it difficult to get in two servings of probiotics foods each day, or just don't care for them, feel free to substitute one or both servings with a probiotic supplement. Just make sure it contains 10 to 20 billion colony-forming units (CFUs) and store it as instructed on the label.

WEIGHT

WATER INTAKE

number of 240-ml/
8-fl-oz glasses

☐ ☐ ☐ ☐
☐ ☐ ☐ ☐

FOOD INTAKE

number of servings

☐ Lean Proteins

☐ Cleansing
Vegetables

☐ Low Sugar Fruit
(2 servings)

☐ Probiotic Foods
(2 servings)

☐ Friendly Fats
(1–2 tablespoons)

Breakfast

Lunch

Dinner

Snacks

Dr Mike's Workout Tip of the Day

Think you are too stressed out to exercise? Once you start exercising on a daily basis, you will find yourself feeling more relaxed and less stressed. Increased activity through exercise causes the brain to release more serotonin, a natural mood elevator, and can be the best remedy when you feel depression coming on.

Cardio

TIME	ACTIVITY DESCRIPTION	DURATION	CALORIES BURNT	DISTANCE	STEPS

Toning Exercises

EXERCISES	SETS	REPS	WEIGHT	TIME	CALORIES BURNT

DAY 12 – MY DAILY JOURNAL

What worked well?

_____
_____
_____

What didn't work well?

_____
_____
_____

I experienced the following changes:

_____
_____
_____

Ways to overcome these challenges
(brainstorm as many problem solvers as you can):

_____
_____
_____

From your list choose the best solutions and develop
strategies for success.

_____
_____
_____

Reflections: Write in your journal how you're feeling, your successes, anything that comes to mind about your progress so far. Read through *The 17 Day Diet* book to learn about all my strategies for overcoming barriers. Which ones can you apply today?

_____
_____
_____
_____
_____
_____

DAY 13 – MY DAILY FOOD CHART   DATE

Dr Mike's Food Tip of the Day

If you're taking statins – a prescription medicine taken to lower cholesterol – you may think eating grapefruit is off-limits. Whilst it's true that
an interaction was discovered in the nineties, the amount and the time
of day it is consumed is key. Consult your doctor about whether you
might eat a limited amount of grapefruit (i.e., ½ grapefruit) in the
morning and then take statins in the evening.

WEIGHT

WATER INTAKE

number of 240-ml/
8-fl-oz glasses

☐ ☐ ☐ ☐
☐ ☐ ☐ ☐

FOOD INTAKE

number of servings

☐ Lean Proteins

☐ Cleansing
Vegetables

☐ Low Sugar Fruit
(2 servings)

☐ Probiotic Foods
(2 servings)

☐ Friendly Fats
(1–2 tablespoons)

Breakfast

_____
_____
_____
_____
_____

Lunch

_____
_____
_____
_____
_____

Dinner

_____
_____
_____
_____

Snacks

_____
_____
_____

Dr Mike's Workout Tip of the Day

Today's best reason to complete your 17 minute workout: it slows down some aspects of the ageing process. Whilst your peers may begin to experience aches and pains from inactivity, you will be strengthening your muscles and joints and improving your flexibility and your ability to maintain an active lifestyle.

Cardio

TIME	ACTIVITY DESCRIPTION	DURATION	CALORIES BURNT	DISTANCE	STEPS

Toning Exercises

EXERCISES	SETS	REPS	WEIGHT	TIME	CALORIES BURNT

DAY 13 – MY DAILY JOURNAL

What worked well?

_____

_____

_____

What didn't work well?

_____

_____

_____

I experienced the following changes:

_____

_____

_____

Ways to overcome these challenges
(brainstorm as many problem solvers as you can):

_____

_____

_____

From your list choose the best solutions and develop
strategies for success.

_____

_____

_____

Reflections: Write in your journal how you're feeling, your successes, anything that comes to mind about your progress so far. Read through *The 17 Day Diet* book to learn about all my strategies for overcoming barriers. Which ones can you apply today?

_____

_____

_____

_____

_____

_____

DAY 14 – MY DAILY FOOD CHART   DATE

Dr Mike's Food Tip of the Day

Even though you are free to use 1–2 tablespoons of olive oil or linseed oil daily as a 'friendly fat', 1 tablespoon of any kind of oil contains 14 grams of fat. Instead, use fat-free cooking spray to drastically cut fat from your diet. There are several varieties, including olive oil and rape-seed oil. For stir-fry dishes that require higher heat, look for a 'professional' cooking spray, designed to be used at high temperatures.

WEIGHT

WATER INTAKE

number of 240-ml/
8-fl-oz glasses

☐ ☐ ☐ ☐
☐ ☐ ☐ ☐

FOOD INTAKE

number of servings

☐ Lean Proteins

☐ Cleansing
   Vegetables

☐ Low Sugar Fruit
   (2 servings)

☐ Probiotic Foods
   (2 servings)

☐ Friendly Fats
   (1–2 tablespoons)

Breakfast

Lunch

Dinner

Snacks

Dr Mike's Workout Tip of the Day

Are you sick and tired of being sick and tired? Exercise boosts immune function so you will come down with fewer colds and bounce back from them sooner. This boost comes from improved blood flow, which flushes away toxins from muscles and organs. It also helps remove germs and circulates antibodies that fight infection.

Cardio

TIME	ACTIVITY DESCRIPTION	DURATION	CALORIES BURNT	DISTANCE	STEPS

Toning Exercises

EXERCISES	SETS	REPS	WEIGHT	TIME	CALORIES BURNT

DAY 14 – MY DAILY JOURNAL

What worked well?

_____

_____

_____

What didn't work well?

_____

_____

_____

I experienced the following changes:

_____

_____

_____

Ways to overcome these challenges
(brainstorm as many problem solvers as you can):

_____

_____

_____

From your list choose the best solutions and develop
strategies for success.

_____

_____

_____

Reflections: Write in your journal how you're feeling, your successes,
anything that comes to mind about your progress so far. Read through
The 17 Day Diet book to learn about all my strategies for overcoming
barriers. Which ones can you apply today?

_____

_____

_____

_____

_____

_____

DAY 15 – MY DAILY FOOD CHART   DATE

Dr Mike's Food Tip of the Day

Natural list-makers start each day with a 'to do' list. Are you one of them? If you aren't already doing your food shopping from a list, now's the time to start! Before you enter your supermarket, make sure you have your list. Include all the food items you will need for the coming week, based on the 17 Sample Menus from *The 17 Day Diet* or create your own based on guidelines in the book. Check out my comprehensive Shopping List, beginning on page 265.

WEIGHT

WATER INTAKE

number of 240-ml/
8-fl-oz glasses

☐ ☐ ☐ ☐
☐ ☐ ☐ ☐

FOOD INTAKE

number of servings

☐ Lean Proteins

☐ Cleansing
Vegetables

☐ Low Sugar Fruit
(2 servings)

☐ Probiotic Foods
(2 servings)

☐ Friendly Fats
(1–2 tablespoons)

Breakfast

_____

_____

_____

_____

_____

Lunch

_____

_____

_____

_____

Dinner

_____

_____

_____

_____

Snacks

_____

_____

_____

Dr Mike's Workout Tip of the Day

Do you need to go shoe shopping? Having the right type of exercise shoes is so important and often overlooked until foot problems begin to appear. Shop for a shoe that fits well, with room for your toes to wiggle freely. Your heel should not slide in and out of the shoe when tied tightly, and should be designed for your particular activity.

Cardio

TIME	ACTIVITY DESCRIPTION	DURATION	CALORIES BURNT	DISTANCE	STEPS

Toning Exercises

EXERCISES	SETS	REPS	WEIGHT	TIME	CALORIES BURNT

DAY 15 – MY DAILY JOURNAL

What worked well?

_____

_____

_____

What didn't work well?

_____

_____

_____

I experienced the following changes:

_____

_____

_____

Ways to overcome these challenges
(brainstorm as many problem solvers as you can):

_____

_____

_____

From your list choose the best solutions and develop
strategies for success.

_____

_____

_____

Reflections: Write in your journal how you're feeling, your successes, anything that comes to mind about your progress so far. Read through *The 17 Day Diet* book to learn about all my strategies for overcoming barriers. Which ones can you apply today?

_____

_____

_____

_____

_____

_____

DAY 16 – MY DAILY FOOD CHART   DATE

Dr Mike's Food Tip of the Day

Removing the skin on chicken and turkey reduces fat content more than you might think. A 100-g/3½-oz portion of roast chicken contains 13.6 grams with skin, 7.4 grams of fat without skin. That same portion of white meat turkey is 6.3 grams of fat with skin, 3.2 grams of fat without skin. Choosing dark meat turkey ups the fat ante to 11.5 grams fat with, but 7.2 grams without.

WEIGHT

WATER INTAKE

number of 240-ml/
8-fl-oz glasses

☐ ☐ ☐ ☐
☐ ☐ ☐ ☐

FOOD INTAKE

number of servings

☐ Lean Proteins

☐ Cleansing
   Vegetables

☐ Low Sugar Fruit
   (2 servings)

☐ Probiotic Foods
   (2 servings)

☐ Friendly Fats
   (1–2 tablespoons)

Breakfast

_____
_____
_____
_____
_____

Lunch

_____
_____
_____
_____

Dinner

_____
_____
_____
_____
_____

Snacks

_____
_____
_____

Dr Mike's Workout Tip of the Day

Exercise clothing for warm weather and indoor workouts should be comfortable and lightweight. Look for clothing that breathes well, dries quickly and allows you to move your body freely whilst exercising. Cold-weather exercise clothing should be insulating to keep you warm. Dress in layers with a lightweight, breathable layer closest to the skin, followed by an insulating top layer.

Cardio

TIME	ACTIVITY DESCRIPTION	DURATION	CALORIES BURNT	DISTANCE	STEPS

Toning Exercises

EXERCISES	SETS	REPS	WEIGHT	TIME	CALORIES BURNT

DAY 16 – MY DAILY JOURNAL

What worked well?

_____

_____

_____

What didn't work well?

_____

_____

_____

I experienced the following changes:

_____

_____

_____

Ways to overcome these challenges
(brainstorm as many problem solvers as you can):

_____

_____

_____

From your list choose the best solutions and develop
strategies for success.

_____

_____

_____

Reflections: Write in your journal how you're feeling, your successes, anything that comes to mind about your progress so far. Read through *The 17 Day Diet* book to learn about all my strategies for overcoming barriers. Which ones can you apply today?

_____

_____

_____

_____

_____

_____

DAY 17 – MY DAILY FOOD CHART   DATE

Dr Mike's Food Tip of the Day

Check the label of foods labelled fat-free. They are not always a healthy choice! When fat is removed, sugar is sometimes added. The result is a food that is high in calories and low in nutrients.

WEIGHT

WATER INTAKE

number of 240-ml/
8-fl-oz glasses

☐ ☐ ☐ ☐
☐ ☐ ☐ ☐

FOOD INTAKE

number of servings

☐ Lean Proteins

☐ Cleansing
Vegetables

☐ Low Sugar Fruit
(2 servings)

☐ Probiotic Foods
(2 servings)

☐ Friendly Fats
(1–2 tablespoons)

Breakfast

_____

_____

_____

_____

_____

Lunch

_____

_____

_____

_____

_____

Dinner

_____

_____

_____

_____

Snacks

_____

_____

_____

Dr Mike's Workout Tip of the Day

Walking has long been identified as the best form of exercise for just about everyone. It requires no equipment (except those shoes I just talked about), is a low-impact exercise, can be done indoors or outdoors and can help you achieve a multitude of health benefits. Your 17-minute daily walk can reduce your heart attack risk by the same percentage as your jogging friends.

Cardio

TIME	ACTIVITY DESCRIPTION	DURATION	CALORIES BURNT	DISTANCE	STEPS

Toning Exercises

EXERCISES	SETS	REPS	WEIGHT	TIME	CALORIES BURNT

DAY 17 – MY DAILY JOURNAL

What worked well?

_____

_____

_____

What didn't work well?

_____

_____

_____

I experienced the following changes:

_____

_____

_____

Ways to overcome these challenges
(brainstorm as many problem solvers as you can):

_____

_____

_____

From your list choose the best solutions and develop
strategies for success.

_____

_____

_____

Reflections: Write in your journal how you're feeling, your successes,
anything that comes to mind about your progress so far. Read through
The 17 Day Diet book to learn about all my strategies for overcoming
barriers. Which ones can you apply today?

_____

_____

_____

_____

_____

_____

Review: Weight Loss Checklist – Cycle 1

Do any of these apply to you? Read through these statements and answer (truthfully!) to gauge your progress during Cycle 1.

1. Am I accurately recording everything I am eating?

   ☐ **Always**   ☐ **Sometimes**   ☐ **Rarely or Never**

2. Am I weighing myself three to four days a week?

   ☐ **Always**   ☐ **Sometimes**   ☐ **Rarely or Never**

3. Am I eating regular meals and snacks as outlined on the 17 Day Diet?

   ☐ **Always**   ☐ **Sometimes**   ☐ **Rarely or Never**

4. Am I eating the proper foods on this cycle?

   ☐ **Always**   ☐ **Sometimes**   ☐ **Rarely or Never**

5. Am I completing at least 17 minutes of daily exercise?

   ☐ **Always**   ☐ **Sometimes**   ☐ **Rarely or Never**

My top areas to work on in the next cycle:

_____

_____

_____

_____

I lost _____ kg/lb on Cycle 1.

How do you feel about your weight loss?

_____

_____

_____

_____

CYCLE 2

· · · · · · · · · · · · · · · · · · · ·

Activate

GOAL:
· ·

To reset your metabolism through a strategy that involves increasing and decreasing your caloric consumption to stimulate fat-burning and to help prevent plateaus.

What to Eat: The Activate Cycle Food List

On the Activate Cycle, you'll be adding new foods to those you ate on the Accelerate Cycle. These additional foods are listed below.

Proteins

Add in the following foods:

Shellfish

Clams
Crab
Mussels
Lobster
Oysters
Prawns
Scallops

Lean Cuts* of Meat

The leanest cuts are those from the part of the animal that gets the most exercise. Therefore, cuts from the topside, silverside, chuck and flank are the best.

Beef topside
Braising steak
Lean steak mince
Rump steak
Sirloin steak

* Lean cuts tend to be a little tougher. You can tenderise lean cuts by marinating in fat-free liquids like fruit juice, wine, fat-free salad dressings or fat-free broth.

Skirt steak
Pork boneless roast
Pork chops
Pork fillet
Lamb shoulder
Leg of lamb
Veal cutlet

Natural Starches

Grains (1 serving)

Amaranth (100 g/3½ oz)
Barley, pearl (100 g/3½ oz)
Basmati rice (100 g/3½ oz)
Brown rice (100 g/3½ oz)
Bulgar wheat (70 g/2½ oz)
Couscous (100 g/3½ oz)
Millet (100 g/3½ oz)
Oat bran (45 g/1½ oz)
Polenta/cornmeal (70 g/2½ oz)
Porridge oats (45 g/1½ oz)
Quinoa (70 g/2½ oz)

Pulses (1 serving)

Black beans (100 g/3½ oz)
Black-eyed beans (100 g/3½ oz)
Butter beans (100 g/3½ oz)
Chickpeas (125 g/4½ oz)
Kidney beans (100 g/3½ oz)
Haricot beans (100 g/3½ oz)
Lentils (100 g/3½ oz)
Peas (70 g/2½ oz)
Pinto beans (100 g/3½ oz)
Soya beans (100 g/3½ oz)

Split peas (100 g/3½ oz)
Virtually any bean or pulse

Starchy Vegetables (1 serving)

Breadfruit, available in Caribbean grocers (220 g/7¾ oz)
Potato (1 medium)
Sweetcorn (70 g/2½ oz)
Sweet potato (1 medium)
Taro, available in Caribbean grocers (55 g/2 oz)
Winter squashes, acorn, butternut, etc. (65 g/2¼ oz))
Yam (1 medium)

Cleansing Vegetables

(Same foods as Accelerate Cycle)

Low-Sugar Fruits

(Same foods as Accelerate Cycle)

Probiotics

(Same foods as Accelerate Cycle)

Friendly Fats

(Same foods as Accelerate Cycle)

Condiments

Condiments and seasonings are allowed in moderation: salsa, low-carb pasta sauce, light soy sauce, reduced-sugar tomato ketchup, fat-free soured cream, low-fat, low-sodium broth, a natural low-calorie sweetener, sugar-free jams and jellies, vegetable cooking spray, fat-free cheeses (i.e. Parmesan), fat-free salad dressing, salt, pepper, vinegar, mustard, herbs and spices.

Meal Planning Made Easy

On the Activate Cycle you alternate Accelerate Cycle days with Activate Cycle days. On Activate days you eat:

- Liberal amounts of protein and cleansing vegetables.
- Two daily servings of natural starches (carbohydrates).
- Two low-sugar fruit servings.
- Two servings of probiotic foods.
- One daily serving of friendly fat.

Here's a sample menu for Cycle 2:

Wake-up drink

Every morning, as soon as you rise, drink one 240-ml/8-fl-oz cup of hot water. Squeeze half a lemon into the cup; the lemon stimulates your digestive juices. Your goal is to drink at least six to seven more glasses of water by the end of the day.

Day 1

Breakfast

- 1 Dr Mike's Power Cookie (see *The 17 Day Diet* for recipe)
- 1 fresh peach, sliced
- 1 cup green tea

Lunch

- Chicken salad: baked or grilled chicken breast (diced), looseleaf lettuce, 1 sliced tomato, assorted salad veggies, 2 tablespoons olive oil mixed with 4 tablespoons balsamic vinegar
- 90 g/3¼ oz brown rice
- 175 g/6 oz sugar-free fruit-flavoured yoghurt

Dinner

- Grilled salmon
- Steamed veggies

Snacks

- Peach Smoothie (See the recipes on pages 287–294.)

The next day, day 2, follow the Accelerate Cycle menu.

DAY 1 – MY DAILY FOOD CHART   DATE

Dr Mike's Food Tip of the Day

Shellfish – crab, clams, mussels, oysters, scallops and prawns – are new foods that have been added in Cycle 2 on Activate days. As long as you don't have an allergy, enjoy shellfish steamed or broiled, for a low-fat, low-cholesterol heart-healthy choice that is also a good source of protein and is full of vitamins and minerals. Shellfish also contain omega-3 fatty acids, although levels are not as high as in fatty fish like salmon and tuna.

WEIGHT

WATER INTAKE

number of 240-ml/
8-fl-oz glasses

☐ ☐ ☐ ☐
☐ ☐ ☐ ☐

FOOD INTAKE

number of servings

☐ Lean Proteins

☐ Cleansing
Vegetables

☐ Natural Starch
(2 servings on
Activate days)

☐ Low Sugar Fruit
(2 servings)

☐ Probiotic Foods
(2 servings)

☐ Friendly Fats
(1–2 tablespoons)

Breakfast

_____
_____
_____
_____
_____

Lunch

_____
_____
_____
_____

Dinner

_____
_____
_____
_____

Snacks

_____
_____
_____

Dr Mike's Workout Tip of the Day

Are your shins aching? This is a common problem for new walkers and one that can be avoided. Make sure you are increasing your speed and distance gradually. Before and after your walk, perform ankle circles and toe points as part of your stretch routine, then stretch your calves and shins after you walk. Last but not least, make sure you are wearing well-fitting walking shoes.

Cardio

TIME	ACTIVITY DESCRIPTION	DURATION	CALORIES BURNT	DISTANCE	STEPS

Toning Exercises

EXERCISES	SETS	REPS	WEIGHT	TIME	CALORIES BURNT

DAY 1 – MY DAILY JOURNAL

What worked well?

_____

_____

_____

What didn't work well?

_____

_____

_____

I experienced the following changes:

_____

_____

_____

Ways to overcome these challenges
(brainstorm as many problem solvers as you can):

_____

_____

_____

From your list choose the best solutions and develop
strategies for success.

_____

_____

_____

Reflections: Write in your journal how you're feeling, your successes,
anything that comes to mind about your progress so far. Read through
The 17 Day Diet book to learn about all my strategies for overcoming
barriers. Which ones can you apply today?

_____

_____

_____

_____

_____

_____

DAY 2 – MY DAILY FOOD CHART   DATE

Dr Mike's Food Tip of the Day

Here's a tip for trimming all visible fat from meat: just place it in the
freezer for 15–20 minutes, enough time for the fat to begin to harden.
Your trimming job will be much easier!

WEIGHT

WATER INTAKE

number of 240-ml/
8-fl-oz glasses

☐ ☐ ☐ ☐
☐ ☐ ☐ ☐

FOOD INTAKE

number of servings

☐ Lean Proteins

☐ Cleansing
  Vegetables

☐ Natural Starch
  (2 servings on
  Activate days)

☐ Low Sugar Fruit
  (2 servings)

☐ Probiotic Foods
  (2 servings)

☐ Friendly Fats
  (1–2 tablespoons)

Breakfast

_____

_____

_____

_____

_____

Lunch

_____

_____

_____

_____

Dinner

_____

_____

_____

_____

Snacks

_____

_____

_____

Dr Mike's Workout Tip of the Day

Have you thought of purchasing a pedometer to measure your steps? Studies published in the *Journal of the American Medical Association* show people who use a pedometer (also called a step counter) are more active, lose weight and are able to lower their blood pressure, especially if they are given a goal to increase their number of daily steps.

Cardio

TIME	ACTIVITY DESCRIPTION	DURATION	CALORIES BURNT	DISTANCE	STEPS

Toning Exercises

EXERCISES	SETS	REPS	WEIGHT	TIME	CALORIES BURNT

DAY 2 – MY DAILY JOURNAL

What worked well?

_____

_____

_____

What didn't work well?

_____

_____

_____

I experienced the following changes:

_____

_____

_____

**Ways to overcome these challenges
(brainstorm as many problem solvers as you can):**

_____

_____

_____

**From your list choose the best solutions and develop
strategies for success.**

_____

_____

_____

Reflections: Write in your journal how you're feeling, your successes,
anything that comes to mind about your progress so far. Read through
The 17 Day Diet book to learn about all my strategies for overcoming
barriers. Which ones can you apply today?

_____

_____

_____

_____

_____

_____

_____

DAY 3 – MY DAILY FOOD CHART   DATE

Dr Mike's Food Tip of the Day

Some of the grains added to your food list in Cycle 2 may be new to you. Amaranth, for example, is included in the grain category but is actually a 'pseudograin', making it a desirable food for those with a gluten allergy. Look for amaranth in the natural foods section of your supermarket or at a health foods shops. Note: Amaranth seeds have a higher protein content than wheat!

WEIGHT

WATER INTAKE

number of 240-ml/
8-fl-oz glasses

☐ ☐ ☐ ☐
☐ ☐ ☐ ☐

FOOD INTAKE

number of servings

☐ Lean Proteins

☐ Cleansing
Vegetables

☐ Natural Starch
(2 servings on
Activate days)

☐ Low Sugar Fruit
(2 servings)

☐ Probiotic Foods
(2 servings)

☐ Friendly Fats
(1–2 tablespoons)

Breakfast

_____
_____
_____
_____
_____

Lunch

_____
_____
_____
_____

Dinner

_____
_____
_____
_____

Snacks

_____
_____
_____

Dr Mike's Workout Tip of the Day

Got that pedometer yet? Using one can motivate you to walk more. Set a goal to walk an extra 2,000 steps per day, then check periodically to see if you need more steps for the day.

Cardio

TIME	ACTIVITY DESCRIPTION	DURATION	CALORIES BURNT	DISTANCE	STEPS

Toning Exercises

EXERCISES	SETS	REPS	WEIGHT	TIME	CALORIES BURNT

DAY 3 – MY DAILY JOURNAL

What worked well?

_____
_____
_____

What didn't work well?

_____
_____
_____

I experienced the following changes:

_____
_____
_____

Ways to overcome these challenges
(brainstorm as many problem solvers as you can):

_____
_____
_____

From your list choose the best solutions and develop
strategies for success.

_____
_____
_____

Reflections: Write in your journal how you're feeling, your successes,
anything that comes to mind about your progress so far. Read through
The 17 Day Diet book to learn about all my strategies for overcoming
barriers. Which ones can you apply today?

_____
_____
_____
_____
_____
_____

DAY 4 – MY DAILY FOOD CHART   DATE

Dr Mike's Food Tip of the Day

Be alert to serving sizes! What you used to consider as a serving and what a serving actually is are most likely very different things. See pages 86–87 to find the serving sizes for natural grains, beans/pulses and some starchy veggies. Get out your scales and ensure you weigh them accurately!

WEIGHT

Breakfast

WATER INTAKE

number of 240-ml/
8-fl-oz glasses

☐ ☐ ☐ ☐
☐ ☐ ☐ ☐

FOOD INTAKE

number of servings

Lunch

☐ Lean Proteins

☐ Cleansing
   Vegetables

☐ Natural Starch
   (2 servings on
   Activate days)

Dinner

☐ Low Sugar Fruit
   (2 servings)

☐ Probiotic Foods
   (2 servings)

☐ Friendly Fats
   (1–2 tablespoons)

Snacks

Dr Mike's Workout Tip of the Day

Okay, so I'm passionate about pedometers. If you're still shopping, you'll find that some pedometers just count your steps, some digital ones also measure your distance and others estimate how many calories have been burnt. Pedometers are priced to fit any budget and come with a clip or strap to attach to your waistband or belt.

Cardio

TIME	ACTIVITY DESCRIPTION	DURATION	CALORIES BURNT	DISTANCE	STEPS

Toning Exercises

EXERCISES	SETS	REPS	WEIGHT	TIME	CALORIES BURNT

DAY 4 – MY DAILY JOURNAL

What worked well?

_____
_____
_____

What didn't work well?

_____
_____
_____

I experienced the following changes:

_____
_____
_____

Ways to overcome these challenges
(brainstorm as many problem solvers as you can):

_____
_____
_____

From your list choose the best solutions and develop
strategies for success.

_____
_____
_____

Reflections: Write in your journal how you're feeling, your successes,
anything that comes to mind about your progress so far. Read through
The 17 Day Diet book to learn about all my strategies for overcoming
barriers. Which ones can you apply today?

_____
_____
_____
_____
_____
_____

DAY 5 – MY DAILY FOOD CHART   DATE

Dr Mike's Food Tip of the Day

To get an idea on what a serving size looks like, mental pictures can help. One serving of veggies is about the size of a cricket ball. Think of a serving of grains, pulses or fruit as the size of half a cricketball.

WEIGHT

Breakfast

WATER INTAKE

number of 240-ml/
8-fl-oz glasses

☐ ☐ ☐ ☐
☐ ☐ ☐ ☐

FOOD INTAKE

number of servings

Lunch

☐ Lean Proteins

☐ Cleansing
Vegetables

☐ Natural Starch
(2 servings on
Activate days)

Dinner

☐ Low Sugar Fruit
(2 servings)

☐ Probiotic Foods
(2 servings)

☐ Friendly Fats
(1–2 tablespoons)

Snacks

Dr Mike's Workout Tip of the Day

Don't just sit there! Walking at 3 mph burns about three times the calories that you burn whilst sitting still. At 3 mph, you can walk a mile in about 20 minutes. Up your pace to 4 mph and you'll burn five times the calories of the couch potato that you used to be!

Cardio

TIME	ACTIVITY DESCRIPTION	DURATION	CALORIES BURNT	DISTANCE	STEPS

Toning Exercises

EXERCISES	SETS	REPS	WEIGHT	TIME	CALORIES BURNT

DAY 5 – MY DAILY JOURNAL

What worked well?

_____

_____

_____

What didn't work well?

_____

_____

_____

I experienced the following changes:

_____

_____

_____

**Ways to overcome these challenges
(brainstorm as many problem solvers as you can):**

_____

_____

_____

**From your list choose the best solutions and develop
strategies for success.**

_____

_____

_____

Reflections: Write in your journal how you're feeling, your successes,
anything that comes to mind about your progress so far. Read through
The 17 Day Diet book to learn about all my strategies for overcoming
barriers. Which ones can you apply today?

_____

_____

_____

_____

_____

_____

DAY 6 – MY DAILY FOOD CHART   DATE

Dr Mike's Food Tip of the Day

Quinoa (pronounced keen-wah) is another super-nutritious, gluten-free food that has been added in Cycle 2. Like amaranth, it is also technically a seed and is a complete protein. Found in the natural foods section of your supermarket or at a health foods shop, quinoa has a slightly nutty taste and fluffy texture when boiled.

WEIGHT

WATER INTAKE

number of 240-ml/
8-fl-oz glasses

☐ ☐ ☐ ☐
☐ ☐ ☐ ☐

FOOD INTAKE

number of servings

☐ Lean Proteins

☐ Cleansing
Vegetables

☐ Natural Starch
(2 servings on
Activate days)

☐ Low Sugar Fruit
(2 servings)

☐ Probiotic Foods
(2 servings)

☐ Friendly Fats
(1–2 tablespoons)

Breakfast

_____
_____
_____
_____
_____

Lunch

_____
_____
_____
_____

Dinner

_____
_____
_____
_____

Snacks

_____
_____
_____

Dr Mike's Workout Tip of the Day

It's raining, it's too hot, it's too cold . . . These are oft-heard excuses that are just that – they are excuses! There is always going to be weather! Make sure you have a back-up plan for your daily walk, like indoor walking at an indoor shopping centre or walking on a treadmill at home or at the gym.

Cardio

TIME	ACTIVITY DESCRIPTION	DURATION	CALORIES BURNT	DISTANCE	STEPS

Toning Exercises

EXERCISES	SETS	REPS	WEIGHT	TIME	CALORIES BURNT

DAY 6 – MY DAILY JOURNAL

What worked well?

_____
_____
_____

What didn't work well?

_____
_____
_____

I experienced the following changes:

_____
_____
_____

Ways to overcome these challenges
(brainstorm as many problem solvers as you can):

_____
_____
_____

From your list choose the best solutions and develop
strategies for success.

_____
_____
_____

Reflections: Write in your journal how you're feeling, your successes, anything that comes to mind about your progress so far. Read through *The 17 Day Diet* book to learn about all my strategies for overcoming barriers. Which ones can you apply today?

_____
_____
_____
_____
_____
_____

DAY 7 – MY DAILY FOOD CHART   DATE

Dr Mike's Food Tip of the Day

Drinking eight 240-ml/8-fl-oz glasses of water each day can be a challenge if you have not been used to consuming that much liquid. Try sipping water throughout the day rather than forcing down large quantities at one time. Add a lemon or lime wedge to jazz up the taste of plain water.

WEIGHT

WATER INTAKE

number of 240-ml/
8-fl-oz glasses

☐ ☐ ☐ ☐
☐ ☐ ☐ ☐

FOOD INTAKE

number of servings

☐ Lean Proteins

☐ Cleansing
Vegetables

☐ Natural Starch
(2 servings on
Activate days)

☐ Low Sugar Fruit
(2 servings)

☐ Probiotic Foods
(2 servings)

☐ Friendly Fats
(1–2 tablespoons)

Breakfast

_____
_____
_____
_____
_____
_____

Lunch

_____
_____
_____
_____

Dinner

_____
_____
_____
_____

Snacks

_____
_____
_____

Dr Mike's Workout Tip of the Day

Which do you enjoy more? Walking alone or with others? If you are around people all day long, you may find those 17 minutes of solitude are rejuvenating and provide time for you to be alone with your thoughts. If you spend a lot of time alone, seek out a walking group or at least one other person to make your walk time a social time too.

Cardio

TIME	ACTIVITY DESCRIPTION	DURATION	CALORIES BURNT	DISTANCE	STEPS

Toning Exercises

EXERCISES	SETS	REPS	WEIGHT	TIME	CALORIES BURNT

DAY 7 – MY DAILY JOURNAL

What worked well?

_____

_____

_____

What didn't work well?

_____

_____

_____

I experienced the following changes:

_____

_____

_____

Ways to overcome these challenges
(brainstorm as many problem solvers as you can):

_____

_____

_____

From your list choose the best solutions and develop
strategies for success.

_____

_____

_____

Reflections: Write in your journal how you're feeling, your successes,
anything that comes to mind about your progress so far. Read through
The 17 Day Diet book to learn about all my strategies for overcoming
barriers. Which ones can you apply today?

_____

_____

_____

_____

_____

_____

DAY 8 – MY DAILY FOOD CHART   DATE

Dr Mike's Food Tip of the Day

Craving pasta? Try baking spaghetti squash, a variety of winter squash with a pale yellow rind and stringy flesh that shreds into threads like thin spaghetti or vermicelli. Or bake another variety of winter squash such as acorn or butternut.

WEIGHT

WATER INTAKE

number of 240-ml/
8-fl-oz glasses

☐ ☐ ☐ ☐
☐ ☐ ☐ ☐

FOOD INTAKE

number of servings

☐ Lean Proteins

☐ Cleansing
   Vegetables

☐ Natural Starch
   (2 servings on
   Activate days)

☐ Low Sugar Fruit
   (2 servings)

☐ Probiotic Foods
   (2 servings)

☐ Friendly Fats
   (1–2 tablespoons)

Breakfast

_____
_____
_____
_____
_____

Lunch

_____
_____
_____
_____

Dinner

_____
_____
_____
_____

Snacks

_____
_____
_____

Dr Mike's Workout Tip of the Day

Depending on your current weight, how fast you are walking and whether the terrain is flat or hilly, 100 calories, on average, are burnt walking 1 mile. And that takes about 2,000 steps. Even though your stride will be different from someone else's, an average stride is usually about 60 to 90 cm (2 to 3 ft) in length. That means to complete one mile will take between 1,760 and 2,640 steps.

Cardio

TIME	ACTIVITY DESCRIPTION	DURATION	CALORIES BURNT	DISTANCE	STEPS

Toning Exercises

EXERCISES	SETS	REPS	WEIGHT	TIME	CALORIES BURNT

DAY 8 – MY DAILY JOURNAL

What worked well?

_____

_____

_____

What didn't work well?

_____

_____

_____

I experienced the following changes:

_____

_____

_____

**Ways to overcome these challenges
(brainstorm as many problem solvers as you can):**

_____

_____

_____

**From your list choose the best solutions and develop
strategies for success.**

_____

_____

_____

Reflections: Write in your journal how you're feeling, your successes,
anything that comes to mind about your progress so far. Read through
The 17 Day Diet book to learn about all my strategies for overcoming
barriers. Which ones can you apply today?

_____

_____

_____

_____

_____

_____

DAY 9 – MY DAILY FOOD CHART   DATE

Dr Mike's Food Tip of the Day

Both regular potatoes and sweet potatoes are on the Cycle 2 list for the Activate cycle and both are highly nutritious. Although sweet potatoes are slightly higher in fibre, much higher in vitamin A and slightly higher in vitamin C, both kinds of potatoes are virtually fat-free and are very low in sodium.

WEIGHT

WATER INTAKE

number of 240-ml/
8-fl-oz glasses

☐ ☐ ☐ ☐
☐ ☐ ☐ ☐

FOOD INTAKE

number of servings

☐ Lean Proteins

☐ Cleansing
Vegetables

☐ Natural Starch
(2 servings on
Activate days)

☐ Low Sugar Fruit
(2 servings)

☐ Probiotic Foods
(2 servings)

☐ Friendly Fats
(1–2 tablespoons)

Breakfast

_____
_____
_____
_____
_____

Lunch

_____
_____
_____
_____

Dinner

_____
_____
_____
_____

Snacks

_____
_____
_____

Dr Mike's Workout Tip of the Day

If you experience itchy legs whilst walking, you aren't alone. This is a common amongst those beginning a walking programme. It may be nothing more than poor circulation, which will go away as you continue to increase your activity level. Another cause may be dry skin, made worse by sweating when you exercise. In that case, moisturise before exercising and wear breathable clothing to avoid heat rash.

Cardio

TIME	ACTIVITY DESCRIPTION	DURATION	CALORIES BURNT	DISTANCE	STEPS

Toning Exercises

EXERCISES	SETS	REPS	WEIGHT	TIME	CALORIES BURNT

DAY 9 – MY DAILY JOURNAL

What worked well?

_____

_____

_____

What didn't work well?

_____

_____

_____

I experienced the following changes:

_____

_____

_____

**Ways to overcome these challenges
(brainstorm as many problem solvers as you can):**

_____

_____

_____

**From your list choose the best solutions and develop
strategies for success.**

_____

_____

_____

Reflections: Write in your journal how you're feeling, your successes,
anything that comes to mind about your progress so far. Read through
The 17 Day Diet book to learn about all my strategies for overcoming
barriers. Which ones can you apply today?

_____

_____

_____

_____

_____

_____

DAY 10 – MY DAILY FOOD CHART   DATE

Dr Mike's Food Tip of the Day

If you have always been a 'meat and potatoes' kind of eater, getting used to eating vegetables may be hard for you. Make a promise to yourself that you'll try one new vegetable each week. Experiment! If you've tried cooked broccoli before and didn't like it, try it again in a raw state with a low-fat, low-calorie dip. Grilling vegetables can give them a different taste too, especially when brushed with a low-calorie vinaigrette dressing.

WEIGHT

WATER INTAKE

number of 240-ml/
8-fl-oz glasses

☐ ☐ ☐ ☐
☐ ☐ ☐ ☐

FOOD INTAKE

number of servings

☐ Lean Proteins

☐ Cleansing
  Vegetables

☐ Natural Starch
  (2 servings on
  Activate days)

☐ Low Sugar Fruit
  (2 servings)

☐ Probiotic Foods
  (2 servings)

☐ Friendly Fats
  (1–2 tablespoons)

Breakfast

_____
_____
_____
_____
_____

Lunch

_____
_____
_____
_____
_____

Dinner

_____
_____
_____
_____

Snacks

_____
_____
_____

Dr Mike's Workout Tip of the Day

It's a heart thing! You may be a loving friend and partner, but without regular exercise, you are not being a friend to your heart. Love yourself enough to do all you can to keep your heart pumping efficiently. Walking does just that, along with improving breathing and blood flow and lowering high blood pressure and cholesterol.

Cardio

TIME	ACTIVITY DESCRIPTION	DURATION	CALORIES BURNT	DISTANCE	STEPS

Toning Exercises

EXERCISES	SETS	REPS	WEIGHT	TIME	CALORIES BURNT

DAY 10 – MY DAILY JOURNAL

What worked well?

_____

_____

_____

What didn't work well?

_____

_____

_____

I experienced the following changes:

_____

_____

_____

**Ways to overcome these challenges
(brainstorm as many problem solvers as you can):**

_____

_____

_____

**From your list choose the best solutions and develop
strategies for success.**

_____

_____

_____

Reflections: Write in your journal how you're feeling, your successes,
anything that comes to mind about your progress so far. Read through
The 17 Day Diet book to learn about all my strategies for overcoming
barriers. Which ones can you apply today?

_____

_____

_____

_____

_____

_____

DAY 11 – MY DAILY FOOD CHART   DATE

Dr Mike's Food Tip of the Day

Whilst green tea is a recommended drink (3 cups a day) due to the natural chemicals it contains that increase fat-burning and stimulates calorie-burning, it can be an acquired taste. The good news is that green tea varieties with other flavours added – mint, lemon, jasmine, pomegranate, mango, peach and orange – are readily available and may tempt you to drink more of it.

WEIGHT

WATER INTAKE

number of 240-ml/
8-fl-oz glasses

☐ ☐ ☐ ☐
☐ ☐ ☐ ☐

FOOD INTAKE

number of servings

☐ Lean Proteins

☐ Cleansing
Vegetables

☐ Natural Starch
(2 servings on
Activate days)

☐ Low Sugar Fruit
(2 servings)

☐ Probiotic Foods
(2 servings)

☐ Friendly Fats
(1–2 tablespoons)

Breakfast

_____
_____
_____
_____
_____

Lunch

_____
_____
_____
_____

Dinner

_____
_____
_____

Snacks

_____
_____
_____

Dr Mike's Workout Tip of the Day

Get moving together! Families that exercise together become closer and their relationships improve. If you are an overweight parent, exercising with your spouse and children can help to change the family dynamic as you begin to lead by example. Walking, riding bicycles or playing sports together can help you build new memories and encourage the rest of your family to begin to lead a more active lifestyle.

Cardio

TIME	ACTIVITY DESCRIPTION	DURATION	CALORIES BURNT	DISTANCE	STEPS

Toning Exercises

EXERCISES	SETS	REPS	WEIGHT	TIME	CALORIES BURNT

DAY 11 – MY DAILY JOURNAL

What worked well?

_____
_____
_____

What didn't work well?

_____
_____
_____

I experienced the following changes:

_____
_____
_____

**Ways to overcome these challenges
(brainstorm as many problem solvers as you can):**

_____
_____
_____

**From your list choose the best solutions and develop
strategies for success.**

_____
_____
_____

Reflections: Write in your journal how you're feeling, your successes,
anything that comes to mind about your progress so far. Read through
The 17 Day Diet book to learn about all my strategies for overcoming
barriers. Which ones can you apply today?

_____
_____
_____
_____
_____
_____

DAY 12 – MY DAILY FOOD CHART   DATE

Dr Mike's Food Tip of the Day

Feeling full and feeling fine! On the Activate days of Cycle 2, you're eating two servings of starchy carbs, but they are the natural, slow-digesting kind. Oats, wholegrains, brown rice, beans, pulses and potatoes are all in this category. They take a long time to digest and keep you feeling full and satisfied.

WEIGHT

WATER INTAKE

number of 240-ml/
8-fl-oz glasses

☐ ☐ ☐ ☐
☐ ☐ ☐ ☐

FOOD INTAKE

number of servings

☐ Lean Proteins

☐ Cleansing
Vegetables

☐ Natural Starch
(2 servings on
Activate days)

☐ Low Sugar Fruit
(2 servings)

☐ Probiotic Foods
(2 servings)

☐ Friendly Fats
(1–2 tablespoons)

Breakfast

Lunch

Dinner

Snacks

Dr Mike's Workout Tip of the Day

I can feel it in my bones . . . Are you over 35? If so, you are already beginning to lose bone density, which can eventually lead to osteoporosis. The good news is that exercise preserves bone density and can actually build bone in older adults, whilst a sedentary lifestyle causes a rapid loss of bone density.

Cardio

TIME	ACTIVITY DESCRIPTION	DURATION	CALORIES BURNT	DISTANCE	STEPS

Toning Exercises

EXERCISES	SETS	REPS	WEIGHT	TIME	CALORIES BURNT

DAY 12 – MY DAILY JOURNAL

What worked well?

_____

_____

_____

What didn't work well?

_____

_____

_____

I experienced the following changes:

_____

_____

_____

Ways to overcome these challenges
(brainstorm as many problem solvers as you can):

_____

_____

_____

From your list choose the best solutions and develop
strategies for success.

_____

_____

_____

Reflections: Write in your journal how you're feeling, your successes,
anything that comes to mind about your progress so far. Read through
The 17 Day Diet book to learn about all my strategies for overcoming
barriers. Which ones can you apply today?

_____

_____

_____

_____

_____

_____

DAY 13 – MY DAILY FOOD CHART   DATE

Dr Mike's Food Tip of the Day

I included my Hunger/Fullness Meter in *The 17 Day Diet* book to help you gauge your hunger and fullness. Rating your hunger from being a 'little hungry' to 'stomach growling hungry' can mean the difference between success and failure. Don't let yourself get too hungry! There is no reason to get there. By the same token, don't let your fullness meter get to the 'stuffed' stage! Learn to stop eating when you're not quite full.

WEIGHT

WATER INTAKE

number of 240-ml/
8-fl-oz glasses

☐ ☐ ☐ ☐
☐ ☐ ☐ ☐

FOOD INTAKE

number of servings

☐ Lean Proteins

☐ Cleansing
Vegetables

☐ Natural Starch
(2 servings on
Activate days)

☐ Low Sugar Fruit
(2 servings)

☐ Probiotic Foods
(2 servings)

☐ Friendly Fats
(1–2 tablespoons)

Breakfast

_____
_____
_____
_____
_____

Lunch

_____
_____
_____
_____

Dinner

_____
_____
_____
_____

Snacks

_____
_____
_____

Dr Mike's Workout Tip of the Day

Have you have been walking or engaging in at least 17 minutes of daily exercise since Day 1 (of Cycle 1) of the 17 Day Diet? That means you have now been exercising for a total of 30 days! Bravo! If we were to check your cholesterol today, your LDL (bad) cholesterol level should have fallen by nearly 30 per cent, and that's similar to the decrease seen with some cholesterol-lowering medicines!

Cardio

TIME	ACTIVITY DESCRIPTION	DURATION	CALORIES BURNT	DISTANCE	STEPS

Toning Exercises

EXERCISES	SETS	REPS	WEIGHT	TIME	CALORIES BURNT

DAY 13 – MY DAILY JOURNAL

What worked well?

_____
_____
_____

What didn't work well?

_____
_____
_____

I experienced the following changes:

_____
_____
_____

Ways to overcome these challenges
(brainstorm as many problem solvers as you can):

_____
_____
_____

From your list choose the best solutions and develop
strategies for success.

_____
_____
_____

Reflections: Write in your journal how you're feeling, your successes, anything that comes to mind about your progress so far. Read through *The 17 Day Diet* book to learn about all my strategies for overcoming barriers. Which ones can you apply today?

_____
_____
_____
_____
_____
_____

DAY 14 – MY DAILY FOOD CHART   DATE

Dr Mike's Food Tip of the Day

Glucose-fructose syrup (called high-fructose corn syrup in the US), which is found in soft drinks, meats, cheeses and many other foods, should be limited, along with all other added sweeteners, whenever possible. Get used to checking labels for ingredients. As obesity has risen in our country, so has consumption of glucose-fructose syrup. It quickly turns into body fat and can cause the body to overproduce insulin, which could lead to type 2 diabetes.

WEIGHT

WATER INTAKE

number of 240-ml/
8-fl-oz glasses

☐ ☐ ☐ ☐
☐ ☐ ☐ ☐

FOOD INTAKE

number of servings

☐ Lean Proteins

☐ Cleansing
   Vegetables

☐ Natural Starch
   (2 servings on
   Activate days)

☐ Low Sugar Fruit
   (2 servings)

☐ Probiotic Foods
   (2 servings)

☐ Friendly Fats
   (1–2 tablespoons)

Breakfast

_____
_____
_____
_____
_____

Lunch

_____
_____
_____
_____

Dinner

_____
_____
_____
_____

Snacks

_____
_____
_____

Dr Mike's Workout Tip of the Day

Shake it up! After a while, you may become bored with doing the same thing day after day. Even if you enjoy walking, you may need to change your route, the time of day you walk or the entire surroundings of your walk. Drive to a local park or visit the botanical gardens or the zoo to get plenty of exercise whilst stimulating your senses with the beauty around you.

Cardio

TIME	ACTIVITY DESCRIPTION	DURATION	CALORIES BURNT	DISTANCE	STEPS

Toning Exercises

EXERCISES	SETS	REPS	WEIGHT	TIME	CALORIES BURNT

DAY 14 – MY DAILY JOURNAL

What worked well?

_____

_____

_____

What didn't work well?

_____

_____

_____

I experienced the following changes:

_____

_____

_____

**Ways to overcome these challenges
(brainstorm as many problem solvers as you can):**

_____

_____

_____

**From your list choose the best solutions and develop
strategies for success.**

_____

_____

_____

Reflections: Write in your journal how you're feeling, your successes,
anything that comes to mind about your progress so far. Read through
The 17 Day Diet book to learn about all my strategies for overcoming
barriers. Which ones can you apply today?

_____

_____

_____

_____

_____

_____

DAY 15 – MY DAILY FOOD CHART   DATE

Dr Mike's Food Tip of the Day

Visualise a particular food superglued to your bum, hips or tummy.
Now imagine how gross it's going to taste with superglue on it. Until
superglue creates new flavours, this should work to keep you away
from fattening goodies.

WEIGHT

WATER INTAKE

number of 240-ml/
8-fl-oz glasses

☐ ☐ ☐ ☐
☐ ☐ ☐ ☐

FOOD INTAKE

number of servings

☐ Lean Proteins

☐ Cleansing
Vegetables

☐ Natural Starch
(2 servings on
Activate days)

☐ Low Sugar Fruit
(2 servings)

☐ Probiotic Foods
(2 servings)

☐ Friendly Fats
(1–2 tablespoons)

Breakfast

_____
_____
_____
_____
_____

Lunch

_____
_____
_____
_____

Dinner

_____
_____
_____
_____

Snacks

_____
_____
_____

Dr Mike's Workout Tip of the Day

Before you miss your workout, ask yourself: will I regret it later? Think about how you'll feel when you get into bed tonight knowing you have let yourself down by not taking at least 17 minutes out of your day to move your body! Instead of caving in to instant gratification, think about how you'll feel about yourself after you live up to your commitment to exercise daily.

Cardio

TIME	ACTIVITY DESCRIPTION	DURATION	CALORIES BURNT	DISTANCE	STEPS

Toning Exercises

EXERCISES	SETS	REPS	WEIGHT	TIME	CALORIES BURNT

DAY 15 – MY DAILY JOURNAL

What worked well?

_____

_____

_____

What didn't work well?

_____

_____

_____

I experienced the following changes:

_____

_____

_____

Ways to overcome these challenges
(brainstorm as many problem solvers as you can):

_____

_____

_____

From your list choose the best solutions and develop
strategies for success.

_____

_____

_____

Reflections: Write in your journal how you're feeling, your successes, anything that comes to mind about your progress so far. Read through *The 17 Day Diet* book to learn about all my strategies for overcoming barriers. Which ones can you apply today?

_____

_____

_____

_____

_____

_____

DAY 16 – MY DAILY FOOD CHART   DATE

Dr Mike's Food Tip of the Day

How are you enjoying your wake-up drink – a 240-ml/8-fl-oz cup of hot water with half a lemon squeezed into it? Not only is it the first of the eight glasses of water you are to drink by the end of the day, but it stimulates your digestive juices and rehydrates your body after a night's sleep so you can properly absorb nutrients from the food you'll eat throughout the day. Now, go ahead and enjoy a cup of green tea, or if you must, that cup of coffee!

WEIGHT

WATER INTAKE

number of 240-ml/
8-fl-oz glasses

☐ ☐ ☐ ☐
☐ ☐ ☐ ☐

FOOD INTAKE

number of servings

☐ Lean Proteins

☐ Cleansing
Vegetables

☐ Natural Starch
(2 servings on
Activate days)

☐ Low Sugar Fruit
(2 servings)

☐ Probiotic Foods
(2 servings)

☐ Friendly Fats
(1–2 tablespoons)

Breakfast

_____
_____
_____
_____
_____

Lunch

_____
_____
_____
_____

Dinner

_____
_____
_____
_____

Snacks

_____
_____
_____

Dr Mike's Workout Tip of the Day

Use the talk test: if you aren't sure you are walking fast enough to increase your heart rate and your fitness level, take the talk test. If you can sing along with that favourite song you're listening to on your iPod, you are walking too slowly. If you can't carry on a simple conversation with your walking partner and are gasping for breath as you walk, you are walking too fast.

Cardio

TIME	ACTIVITY DESCRIPTION	DURATION	CALORIES BURNT	DISTANCE	STEPS

Toning Exercises

EXERCISES	SETS	REPS	WEIGHT	TIME	CALORIES BURNT

DAY 16 – MY DAILY JOURNAL

What worked well?

_____

_____

_____

What didn't work well?

_____

_____

_____

I experienced the following changes:

_____

_____

_____

Ways to overcome these challenges
(brainstorm as many problem solvers as you can):

_____

_____

_____

From your list choose the best solutions and develop
strategies for success.

_____

_____

_____

Reflections: Write in your journal how you're feeling, your successes,
anything that comes to mind about your progress so far. Read through
The 17 Day Diet book to learn about all my strategies for overcoming
barriers. Which ones can you apply today?

_____

_____

_____

_____

_____

_____

DAY 17 – MY DAILY FOOD CHART   DATE

Dr Mike's Food Tip of the Day

Just like us, the parts of the animal that are the leanest are those that get the most exercise. When choosing lean cuts of meat, remember that they may need to be tenderised to keep them moist and flavourful. Marinating meats in fat-free broth, fat-free salad dressings, wine or fruit juice can transform a lean cut of meat from tough to tasty!

WEIGHT

WATER INTAKE

number of 240-ml/
8-fl-oz glasses

☐ ☐ ☐ ☐
☐ ☐ ☐ ☐

FOOD INTAKE

number of servings

☐ Lean Proteins

☐ Cleansing
Vegetables

☐ Natural Starch
(2 servings on
Activate days)

☐ Low Sugar Fruit
(2 servings)

☐ Probiotic Foods
(2 servings)

☐ Friendly Fats
(1–2 tablespoons)

Breakfast

_____
_____
_____
_____
_____

Lunch

_____
_____
_____
_____

Dinner

_____
_____
_____
_____

Snacks

_____
_____
_____

Dr Mike's Workout Tip of the Day

Men and women who weigh the same amount burn approximately the same number of calories if they complete the same activity. But in so many ways, men and women's exercise preferences differ. Men tend to shy away from the group exercise classes that women enjoy, preferring to go it alone in the gym or participate in an athletic-based activity that doesn't require flexibility or coordination.

Cardio

TIME	ACTIVITY DESCRIPTION	DURATION	CALORIES BURNT	DISTANCE	STEPS

Toning Exercises

EXERCISES	SETS	REPS	WEIGHT	TIME	CALORIES BURNT

DAY 17 – MY DAILY JOURNAL

What worked well?

_____

_____

_____

What didn't work well?

_____

_____

_____

I experienced the following changes:

_____

_____

_____

**Ways to overcome these challenges
(brainstorm as many problem solvers as you can):**

_____

_____

_____

**From your list choose the best solutions and develop
strategies for success.**

_____

_____

_____

Reflections: Write in your journal how you're feeling, your successes,
anything that comes to mind about your progress so far. Read through
The 17 Day Diet book to learn about all my strategies for overcoming
barriers. Which ones can you apply today?

_____

_____

_____

_____

_____

_____

Review: Weight Loss Checklist – Cycle 2

It is only natural that you may experience obstacles as you move through each cycle of the 17 Day Diet. Ask yourself whether you may be sabotaging your success by getting off track in one of these ways:

1. Am I skipping meals, then overeating later in the day?

   ☐ **Always**   ☐ **Sometimes**   ☐ **Rarely or Never**

2. Am I taking second helpings?

   ☐ **Always**   ☐ **Sometimes**   ☐ **Rarely or Never**

3. Am I planning my meals in advance and sticking to my plan?

   ☐ **Always**   ☐ **Sometimes**   ☐ **Rarely or Never**

4. Am I watching television while eating?

   ☐ **Always**   ☐ **Sometimes**   ☐ **Rarely or Never**

5. Am I letting other things distract me from working out every day?

   ☐ **Always**   ☐ **Sometimes**   ☐ **Rarely or Never**

My top areas to work on in the next cycle:

_____

_____

_____

_____

I lost _____ kg/lb on Cycle 2.

How do you feel about your weight loss so far?

_____

_____

_____

_____

CYCLE 3

. . . .

Achieve

GOAL:

To develop good eating habits through the reintroduction of additional foods and move you closer to your goal weight.

What to Eat: The Achieve Cycle Expanded Food List

Where indicated, add foods to your diet, in addition to those you ate on the first 2 cycles.

Proteins

(1 serving = 4 to 6 ounces, or the amount that can fit in the palm of your hand)

Fish and shellfish *(from Accelerate and Activate lists)*
Lean meats *(from Accelerate and Activate lists)*
Poultry *(from Accelerate and Activate lists, including eggs and egg whites)*
Additional poultry:
Quail
Pheasant
Poussin
Reduced-fat turkey bacon or sausage or lunch meat
Lean back bacon

Natural Starches

Breads (1 slice = 1 serving)
Cracked wheat
Fibre-enriched bread
Gluten-free bread
Multigrain bread
Oat bran bread
Sugar-free bread
Pumpernickel
Rye bread
Wholegrain bagel (½ = 1 serving)

Wholegrain pitta bread, 1 pocket

Wholegrain tortilla, 25 cm/10 in

High Fibre Cereals (1 serving)

All-Bran (55 g/2 oz)

All-Bran Bran Buds (55 g/2 oz)

Fibre One (55 g/2 oz)

Gluten-free cold cereals (55 g/2 oz)

Low-sugar muesli (45 g/1½ oz)

Pasta: (1 serving)

Whole-wheat pasta (55 g/2 oz)

Gluten-free pasta (55 g/2 oz)

Vegetable-based pasta (55 g/2 oz)

High-fibre pasta (55 g/2 oz)

Udon pasta (55 g/2 oz)

Vegetables – Unlimited

All cleansing vegetables

Alfalfa

Broccoli sprouts

Chard

Chillies

Coriander

Courgettes

Fennel

Grape vine leaves

Kelp and other edible seaweeds

Kohlrabi

Mangetout

Radishes

Rhubarb

Swede

Summer squash

Yellow runner beans
Virtually any vegetable

Fruits (2 servings daily; Serving = 1 piece fresh or 1 cup chopped fresh fruit)

Apricots

Bananas

Cherries

Currants

Figs

Kiwi

Kumquats

Guava

Mango

Papaya

Pineapple

Pomegranate

Tangerine

Virtually any fresh fruit

Note: If you are watching your sugar intake, stick to lower sugar fruits. These include apples, berries (all varieties), cherries, grapefruit, orange, peach, pear and plum.

Probiotics, Dairy and Dairy Substitutes: 1 to 2 servings daily

Note: Some people don't like dairy foods or can't digest them properly. If you're one of them, try dairy substitutes instead (see below). Try to eat at least one serving daily from this list whilst on the Achieve Cycle.

Probiotic foods from Accelerate and Activate Cycles (1 serving)

Low-calorie cheeses: Brie, Camembert, fontina, low-fat Cheddar, Edam, feta, goat, and low-fat mozzarella (55 g/2 oz)

Low-fat cottage cheese (115 g/4 oz)

Semi-skimmed or skimmed milk (240 ml/8 fl oz)

Low-fat ricotta cheese (115 g/4 oz)

Dairy substitutes: sugar-free rice, almond or soya milk (240 ml/8 fl oz)

Friendly Fats – 1 to 2 tablespoons daily, unless where indicated

Avocado (¼ fruit = 1 serving)

Rapeseed oil (1 tablespoon = 1 serving)

Walnut oil (1 tablespoon = 1 serving)

Light mayonnaise (2 tablespoons = 1 serving)

Mayonnaise (1 tablespoon = 1 serving)

Nuts or seeds, unoiled (2 tablespoons = 1 serving)

Reduced-calorie margarines (2 tablespoons = 1 serving)

Reduced-fat salad dressings (2 tablespoons = 1 serving)

Salad dressings (1 tablespoon = 1 serving)

Trans-free margarines (1 tablespoon = 1 serving)

Optional Snacks

These snacks are all under 100 calories. Plus they're filling and fun to eat.

Babybel low-fat cheese – 2 rounds

Frozen fruit bar

Granola bar, reduced sugar and fat

Microwave popcorn, light (30 g/1 oz)

Skinny Cow ice cream

Sugar-free pudding pot

String cheese – 1 stick

Meal Planning Made Easy

Each day, for the next 17 days, you'll eat:

* Controlled portions of protein from an expanded list (1 serving = 115–175 g/4–6 g, or roughly the amount that can fit in the palm of your hand).

* Liberal amounts of vegetables from an expanded list.

- Two servings of natural starches, high-fibre cereals or pasta from an expanded list.

- Two servings of fruit from an expanded list.

- One to two servings from probiotics, low-fat dairy or dairy substitutes

- One serving of fat from an expanded list.

- Optional snacks.

- Optional daily serving of alcohol.

Here is a sample menu on the Achieve Cycle:

Wake-up drink

Every morning, as soon as you rise, drink one 240-ml/8-fl-oz cup of hot water. Squeeze half a lemon into the cup; the lemon stimulates your digestive juices. Your goal is to drink at least six to seven more glasses of water by the end of the day.

Day 1

Breakfast

- 1 slice brown toast

- 1 poached, soft-boiled or hard-boiled egg

- ½ grapefruit

- 1 cup green tea

Lunch

- Chicken Caesar salad: 115–175 g/4–6 oz grilled chicken breast, cut in pieces, 2 handfuls of Cos lettuce, other desired salad veggies, 2 tablespoons light Caesar dressing

- 1 slice brown toast

- 1 serving fresh fruit

- 1 cup green tea

Dinner

- 115–175 g/4–6 oz roast pork fillet
- 1–2 handfuls of tossed mixed salad with 2 tablespoons fat-free dressing
- 1 cup green tea

Snacks

- 1 probiotic, dairy or dairy substitute serving
- 1 frozen fruit bar

DAY 1 – MY DAILY FOOD CHART   DATE

Dr Mike's Food Tip of the Day

Remember that protein portions in Cycle 3 are to be limited to about the size of a kitchen sponge, a deck of playing cards or the palm of your hand (115–175 g/4–6 oz). Having a visual picture in mind helps you achieve good eating habits for a lifetime including portion control.

WEIGHT

WATER INTAKE

number of 240-ml/
8-fl-oz glasses

☐ ☐ ☐ ☐
☐ ☐ ☐ ☐

FOOD INTAKE

number of servings

☐ Lean Proteins

☐ Cleansing
Vegetables

☐ Natural Starch/
High-Fibre
Cereal/or Pasta
(2 servings)

☐ Fruit (2 servings)

☐ Probiotic Foods/
Dairy/Dairy Subs
(2 servings)

☐ Friendly Fats
(1–2 tablespoons)

☐ Optional snack

Breakfast

_____
_____
_____
_____
_____

Lunch

_____
_____
_____
_____

Dinner

_____
_____
_____
_____

Snacks

_____
_____

Dr Mike's Workout Tip of the Day

Congratulations! You've made it to Cycle 3, and it's time to increase your aerobic exercise! Hopefully you have been slowly increasing your workout time, at least some days of the week, from the minimum of 17 minutes to 30 minutes or longer. If you want to speed up your weight loss during this cycle, strive to do 45 to 60 minutes of aerobic exercise as many days of the week as you can.

Cardio

TIME	ACTIVITY DESCRIPTION	DURATION	CALORIES BURNT	DISTANCE	STEPS

Toning Exercises

EXERCISES	SETS	REPS	WEIGHT	TIME	CALORIES BURNT

DAY 1 – MY DAILY JOURNAL

What worked well?

_____
_____
_____

What didn't work well?

_____
_____
_____

I experienced the following changes:

_____
_____
_____

**Ways to overcome these challenges
(brainstorm as many problem solvers as you can):**

_____
_____
_____

**From your list choose the best solutions and develop
strategies for success.**

_____
_____
_____

Reflections: Write in your journal how you're feeling, your successes,
anything that comes to mind about your progress so far. Read through
The 17 Day Diet book to learn about all my strategies for overcoming
barriers. Which ones can you apply today?

_____
_____
_____
_____
_____
_____

DAY 2 – MY DAILY FOOD CHART   DATE

Dr Mike's Food Tip of the Day

One of the additional poultry choices in Cycle 3 is poussin, a type of domestic chicken that averages 450–680 g/1–1½ lb. Half a hen, cooked with skin removed is 150 calories and 5 gram of fat. With skin, half a hen is 340 calories and a whopping 25 grams of fat! That's why removing skin from all poultry is necessary on the 17 Day Diet.

WEIGHT

WATER INTAKE

number of 240-ml/
8-fl-oz glasses

☐ ☐ ☐ ☐
☐ ☐ ☐ ☐

FOOD INTAKE

number of servings

☐ Lean Proteins

☐ Cleansing
Vegetables

☐ Natural Starch/
High-Fibre
Cereal/or Pasta
(2 servings)

☐ Fruit (2 servings)

☐ Probiotic Foods/
Dairy/Dairy Subs
(2 servings)

☐ Friendly Fats
(1–2 tablespoons)

☐ Optional snack

Breakfast

_____
_____
_____
_____
_____
_____

Lunch

_____
_____
_____
_____
_____

Dinner

_____
_____
_____
_____

Snacks

_____
_____

Dr Mike's Workout Tip of the Day

Aerobics is defined as using the same large muscle group, rhythmically, for a period of 15 to 20 minutes or longer whilst maintaining 60–80 per cent of your maximum heart rate. Any type of aerobic exercise – walking, running, bicycling, swimming, tennis or whatever – can be used to speed up weight loss by creating a calorie deficit: burning more calories than you take in.

Cardio

TIME	ACTIVITY DESCRIPTION	DURATION	CALORIES BURNT	DISTANCE	STEPS

Toning Exercises

EXERCISES	SETS	REPS	WEIGHT	TIME	CALORIES BURNT

DAY 2 – MY DAILY JOURNAL

What worked well?

_____

_____

_____

What didn't work well?

_____

_____

_____

I experienced the following changes:

_____

_____

_____

Ways to overcome these challenges
(brainstorm as many problem solvers as you can):

_____

_____

_____

From your list choose the best solutions and develop
strategies for success.

_____

_____

_____

Reflections: Write in your journal how you're feeling, your successes,
anything that comes to mind about your progress so far. Read through
The 17 Day Diet book to learn about all my strategies for overcoming
barriers. Which ones can you apply today?

_____

_____

_____

_____

_____

_____

_____

DAY 3 – MY DAILY FOOD CHART   DATE

Dr Mike's Food Tip of the Day

Lean back bacon is another new protein choice added in Cycle 3. Choose this type of bacon rather than streaky bacon, which has more fat and calories. Instead of visiting McDonald's try making your own low-fat version of an Egg McMuffin with lean back bacon (50 calories, 2 grams fat per rasher).

WEIGHT

WATER INTAKE

number of 240-ml/
8-fl-oz glasses

☐ ☐ ☐ ☐
☐ ☐ ☐ ☐

FOOD INTAKE

number of servings

☐ Lean Proteins

☐ Cleansing
Vegetables

☐ Natural Starch/
High-Fibre
Cereal/or Pasta
(2 servings)

☐ Fruit (2 servings)

☐ Probiotic Foods/
Dairy/Dairy Subs
(2 servings)

☐ Friendly Fats
(1–2 tablespoons)

☐ Optional snack

Breakfast

_____
_____
_____
_____
_____
_____

Lunch

_____
_____
_____
_____
_____

Dinner

_____
_____
_____
_____

Snacks

_____
_____

Dr Mike's Workout Tip of the Day

Low-impact aerobic activities are best for those with knee problems, as they help tone leg muscles supporting the knee joint that absorb the shock placed on the knee. There are lots of low-impact choices, including walking, swimming, water aerobics, low impact aerobic dance classes, stationary cycling and elliptical training.

Cardio

TIME	ACTIVITY DESCRIPTION	DURATION	CALORIES BURNT	DISTANCE	STEPS

Toning Exercises

EXERCISES	SETS	REPS	WEIGHT	TIME	CALORIES BURNT

DAY 3 – MY DAILY JOURNAL

What worked well?

_____
_____
_____

What didn't work well?

_____
_____
_____

I experienced the following changes:

_____
_____
_____

**Ways to overcome these challenges
(brainstorm as many problem solvers as you can):**

_____
_____
_____

**From your list choose the best solutions and develop
strategies for success.**

_____
_____
_____

Reflections: Write in your journal how you're feeling, your successes,
anything that comes to mind about your progress so far. Read through
The 17 Day Diet book to learn about all my strategies for overcoming
barriers. Which ones can you apply today?

_____
_____
_____
_____
_____
_____
_____

DAY 4 – MY DAILY FOOD CHART   DATE

Dr Mike's Food Tip of the Day

Who's up for popcorn and a film? In Cycle 3 you can enjoy a snack of up to 35 g/1¼ oz of light microwave popcorn. Popcorn is a highly nutritious whole grain that is low calorie (without butter) and contains 40 or more nutrients. It has more protein than any other cereal grain, is iron rich and high in fibre.

WEIGHT

WATER INTAKE

number of 240-ml/
8-fl-oz glasses

☐ ☐ ☐ ☐
☐ ☐ ☐ ☐

FOOD INTAKE

number of servings

☐ Lean Proteins

☐ Cleansing
Vegetables

☐ Natural Starch/
High-Fibre
Cereal/or Pasta
(2 servings)

☐ Fruit (2 servings)

☐ Probiotic Foods/
Dairy/Dairy Subs
(2 servings)

☐ Friendly Fats
(1–2 tablespoons)

☐ Optional snack

Breakfast

_____
_____
_____
_____
_____

Lunch

_____
_____
_____
_____

Dinner

_____
_____
_____
_____

Snacks

_____
_____

Dr Mike's Workout Tip of the Day

Do all you can to avoid exercise injuries! Make sure you have well-fitting shoes especially made for aerobics or cross-training. You need a shoe with lateral support for side-to-side movements, cushioning to absorb impact and proper arch support.

Cardio

TIME	ACTIVITY DESCRIPTION	DURATION	CALORIES BURNT	DISTANCE	STEPS

Toning Exercises

EXERCISES	SETS	REPS	WEIGHT	TIME	CALORIES BURNT

DAY 4 – MY DAILY JOURNAL

What worked well?

_____

_____

_____

What didn't work well?

_____

_____

_____

I experienced the following changes:

_____

_____

_____

Ways to overcome these challenges
(brainstorm as many problem solvers as you can):

_____

_____

_____

From your list choose the best solutions and develop
strategies for success.

_____

_____

_____

Reflections: Write in your journal how you're feeling, your successes,
anything that comes to mind about your progress so far. Read through
The 17 Day Diet book to learn about all my strategies for overcoming
barriers. Which ones can you apply today?

_____

_____

_____

_____

_____

_____

DAY 5 – MY DAILY FOOD CHART   DATE

Dr Mike's Food Tip of the Day

One and only one . . . alcoholic drink, that is. That's a new freedom you've been given in Cycle 3, but portion control applies here too. If you choose to incorporate one glass of wine into your daily diet, that means 150 ml/5 fl oz, not half the bottle! Here's a tip: first pour 150 ml/5 fl oz of water into your wine glass. Then you'll know what 150 ml/5 fl oz looks like!

WEIGHT

WATER INTAKE

number of 240-ml/
8-fl-oz glasses

☐ ☐ ☐ ☐
☐ ☐ ☐ ☐

FOOD INTAKE

number of servings

☐ Lean Proteins

☐ Cleansing
   Vegetables

☐ Natural Starch/
   High-Fibre
   Cereal/or Pasta
   (2 servings)

☐ Fruit (2 servings)

☐ Probiotic Foods/
   Dairy/Dairy Subs
   (2 servings)

☐ Friendly Fats
   (1–2 tablespoons)

☐ Optional snack

Breakfast

_____

_____

_____

_____

_____

Lunch

_____

_____

_____

_____

Dinner

_____

_____

_____

_____

Snacks

_____

_____

Dr Mike's Workout Tip of the Day

If you are walking or jogging outdoors, you are most likely 'pounding the pavement' on concrete, a hard surface that can cause stress injuries like shin splints or tendonitis. But good shoes can help. Walking and jogging on dirt paths or grass is softer, but there can be holes and uneven surfaces to trip you up, so just be careful out there!

Cardio

TIME	ACTIVITY DESCRIPTION	DURATION	CALORIES BURNT	DISTANCE	STEPS

Toning Exercises

EXERCISES	SETS	REPS	WEIGHT	TIME	CALORIES BURNT

DAY 5 – MY DAILY JOURNAL

What worked well?

_____
_____
_____

What didn't work well?

_____
_____
_____

I experienced the following changes:

_____
_____
_____

**Ways to overcome these challenges
(brainstorm as many problem solvers as you can):**

_____
_____
_____

**From your list choose the best solutions and develop
strategies for success.**

_____
_____
_____

Reflections: Write in your journal how you're feeling, your successes,
anything that comes to mind about your progress so far. Read through
The 17 Day Diet book to learn about all my strategies for overcoming
barriers. Which ones can you apply today?

_____
_____
_____
_____
_____
_____

DAY 6 – MY DAILY FOOD CHART   DATE

Dr Mike's Food Tip of the Day

Ah, pasta! Have you been missing it? Combine pasta with nutrient-dense foods, including high-fibre vegetables, beans, fish, poultry and lean meats for a highly nutritious and satisfying meal. Make sure the pasta you choose is wholegrain, high fibre, vegetable based or gluten free.

WEIGHT

WATER INTAKE

number of 240-ml/
8-fl-oz glasses

☐ ☐ ☐ ☐
☐ ☐ ☐ ☐

FOOD INTAKE

number of servings

☐ Lean Proteins

☐ Cleansing
Vegetables

☐ Natural Starch/
High-Fibre
Cereal/or Pasta
(2 servings)

☐ Fruit (2 servings)

☐ Probiotic Foods/
Dairy/Dairy Subs
(2 servings)

☐ Friendly Fats
(1–2 tablespoons)

☐ Optional snack

Breakfast

_____
_____
_____
_____
_____

Lunch

_____
_____
_____
_____

Dinner

_____
_____
_____
_____

Snacks

_____
_____

Dr Mike's Workout Tip of the Day

Avoid the soreness and pain that can be caused by overuse of your
muscles by always starting with a few minutes of warm-up exercises
and ending with a cool down and a final stretch. A warm bath or
shower and a foot soak with Epsom salts will also help to prevent any
possible soreness.

Cardio

TIME	ACTIVITY DESCRIPTION	DURATION	CALORIES BURNT	DISTANCE	STEPS

Toning Exercises

EXERCISES	SETS	REPS	WEIGHT	TIME	CALORIES BURNT

DAY 6 – MY DAILY JOURNAL

What worked well?

_____

_____

_____

What didn't work well?

_____

_____

_____

I experienced the following changes:

_____

_____

_____

**Ways to overcome these challenges
(brainstorm as many problem solvers as you can):**

_____

_____

_____

**From your list choose the best solutions and develop
strategies for success.**

_____

_____

_____

Reflections: Write in your journal how you're feeling, your successes,
anything that comes to mind about your progress so far. Read through
The 17 Day Diet book to learn about all my strategies for overcoming
barriers. Which ones can you apply today?

_____

_____

_____

_____

_____

_____

DAY 7 – MY DAILY FOOD CHART   DATE

Dr Mike's Food Tip of the Day

If you haven't tried udon noodles, a low-fat, cholesterol-free Japanese pan noodle made from wheat flour, put them on your shopping list for next week. Udon noodles are a great addition to a stir-fry dish or Asian soup, and can even be served cold as a salad ingredient.

WEIGHT

WATER INTAKE

number of 240-ml/
8-fl-oz glasses

☐ ☐ ☐ ☐
☐ ☐ ☐ ☐

FOOD INTAKE

number of servings

☐ Lean Proteins

☐ Cleansing
   Vegetables

☐ Natural Starch/
   High-Fibre
   Cereal/or Pasta
   (2 servings)

☐ Fruit (2 servings)

☐ Probiotic Foods/
   Dairy/Dairy Subs
   (2 servings)

☐ Friendly Fats
   (1–2 tablespoons)

☐ Optional snack

Breakfast

_____
_____
_____
_____
_____

Lunch

_____
_____
_____
_____

Dinner

_____
_____
_____
_____

Snacks

_____
_____

Dr Mike's Workout Tip of the Day

Is it best to exercise in the morning or the evening? There is no bad time to exercise, as long as it is a time that works for you! If you have an early morning meeting, just make sure to schedule your workout over your lunch hour or after your workday has ended. Make your workout a priority, and not something that can be cancelled or rescheduled to another day.

Cardio

TIME	ACTIVITY DESCRIPTION	DURATION	CALORIES BURNT	DISTANCE	STEPS

Toning Exercises

EXERCISES	SETS	REPS	WEIGHT	TIME	CALORIES BURNT

DAY 7 – MY DAILY JOURNAL

What worked well?

_____
_____
_____

What didn't work well?

_____
_____
_____

I experienced the following changes:

_____
_____
_____

Ways to overcome these challenges
(brainstorm as many problem solvers as you can):

_____
_____
_____

From your list choose the best solutions and develop
strategies for success.

_____
_____
_____

Reflections: Write in your journal how you're feeling, your successes,
anything that comes to mind about your progress so far. Read through
The 17 Day Diet book to learn about all my strategies for overcoming
barriers. Which ones can you apply today?

_____
_____
_____
_____
_____
_____
_____

DAY 8 – MY DAILY FOOD CHART   DATE

Dr Mike's Food Tip of the Day

Gauge instead of gorge . . . Just because you *can* eat it doesn't mean you should! Remember to gauge how full you are and stop eating before you are stuffed. If you forget (or choose) to leave off your second dairy or carb serving, that's just fine. Cycle 3 is all about learning to listen to your body so you will eat when you are hungry and eat only until you are full.

WEIGHT

WATER INTAKE

number of 240-ml/
8-fl-oz glasses

☐ ☐ ☐ ☐
☐ ☐ ☐ ☐

FOOD INTAKE

number of servings

☐ Lean Proteins

☐ Cleansing
Vegetables

☐ Natural Starch/
High-Fibre
Cereal/or Pasta
(2 servings)

☐ Fruit (2 servings)

☐ Probiotic Foods/
Dairy/Dairy Subs
(2 servings)

☐ Friendly Fats
(1–2 tablespoons)

☐ Optional snack

Breakfast

_____
_____
_____
_____
_____

Lunch

_____
_____
_____
_____
_____

Dinner

_____
_____
_____
_____

Snacks

_____
_____

Dr Mike's Workout Tip of the Day

Regular cardiovascular exercise is not only helping you lose weight but is improving your overall health in multiple ways. Improvements in blood pressure and cholesterol levels, prevention of osteoporosis, heart disease, type 2 diabetes and even some forms of cancer can be attributed to regular physical activity.

Cardio

TIME	ACTIVITY DESCRIPTION	DURATION	CALORIES BURNT	DISTANCE	STEPS

Toning Exercises

EXERCISES	SETS	REPS	WEIGHT	TIME	CALORIES BURNT

DAY 8 – MY DAILY JOURNAL

What worked well?

_____

_____

_____

What didn't work well?

_____

_____

_____

I experienced the following changes:

_____

_____

_____

Ways to overcome these challenges
(brainstorm as many problem solvers as you can):

_____

_____

_____

From your list choose the best solutions and develop
strategies for success.

_____

_____

_____

Reflections: Write in your journal how you're feeling, your successes, anything that comes to mind about your progress so far. Read through *The 17 Day Diet* book to learn about all my strategies for overcoming barriers. Which ones can you apply today?

_____

_____

_____

_____

_____

_____

DAY 9 – MY DAILY FOOD CHART   DATE

Dr Mike's Food Tip of the Day

Are you a reformed 'mindless eater'? Eating whilst watching TV or reading can easily cause you to munch mindlessly. That's why learning portion control is so important to lasting weight-loss success. Measure out the amount of food you are allowed, then eat without guilt!

WEIGHT

WATER INTAKE

number of 240-ml/
8-fl-oz glasses

☐ ☐ ☐ ☐
☐ ☐ ☐ ☐

FOOD INTAKE

number of servings

☐ Lean Proteins

☐ Cleansing
   Vegetables

☐ Natural Starch/
   High-Fibre
   Cereal/or Pasta
   (2 servings)

☐ Fruit (2 servings)

☐ Probiotic Foods/
   Dairy/Dairy Subs
   (2 servings)

☐ Friendly Fats
   (1–2 tablespoons)

☐ Optional snack

Breakfast

_____

_____

_____

_____

_____

Lunch

_____

_____

_____

_____

Dinner

_____

_____

_____

_____

Snacks

_____

_____

Dr Mike's Workout Tip of the Day

Embrace cross-training! Instead of settling into one activity and not deviating from it, try cross-training, which allows you to use different muscle groups, helping to prevent overuse injuries. When your exercise routine includes several different types of exercise, you will be in better condition overall, as different muscles are worked whilst others recover. Try adding a new type of exercise to your routine this week.

Cardio

TIME	ACTIVITY DESCRIPTION	DURATION	CALORIES BURNT	DISTANCE	STEPS

Toning Exercises

EXERCISES	SETS	REPS	WEIGHT	TIME	CALORIES BURNT

DAY 9 – MY DAILY JOURNAL

What worked well?

_____
_____
_____

What didn't work well?

_____
_____
_____

I experienced the following changes:

_____
_____
_____

**Ways to overcome these challenges
(brainstorm as many problem solvers as you can):**

_____
_____
_____

**From your list choose the best solutions and develop
strategies for success.**

_____
_____
_____

Reflections: Write in your journal how you're feeling, your successes,
anything that comes to mind about your progress so far. Read through
The 17 Day Diet book to learn about all my strategies for overcoming
barriers. Which ones can you apply today?

_____
_____
_____
_____
_____
_____

DAY 10 – MY DAILY FOOD CHART   DATE

Dr Mike's Food Tip of the Day

Are you really hungry or could you be thirsty instead? It's easy to know you are thirsty after a workout or when you've just finished mowing the lawn. Sometimes we get a feeling in our stomach that makes us think we are hungry when our body is actually getting a bit dehydrated. Next time you feel that hunger signal, drink a glass of water first. If after a few minutes you still have that empty feeling, follow those hunger pangs to the kitchen for a healthy snack!

WEIGHT

WATER INTAKE

number of 240-ml/
8-fl-oz glasses

☐ ☐ ☐ ☐
☐ ☐ ☐ ☐

FOOD INTAKE

number of servings

☐ Lean Proteins

☐ Cleansing
Vegetables

☐ Natural Starch/
High-Fibre
Cereal/or Pasta
(2 servings)

☐ Fruit (2 servings)

☐ Probiotic Foods/
Dairy/Dairy Subs
(2 servings)

☐ Friendly Fats
(1–2 tablespoons)

☐ Optional snack

Breakfast

_____

_____

_____

_____

_____

Lunch

_____

_____

_____

_____

Dinner

_____

_____

_____

_____

Snacks

_____

_____

Dr Mike's Workout Tip of the Day

Improved digestion and better bowel habits are two benefits of regular exercise. Exercise improves blood circulation and oxygen flow in the body, which helps to keep waste products moving through your digestive system and eliminated without delay. Constipation sufferers often find their condition improves when they exercise on a regular basis along with increasing fibre consumption and water intake.

Cardio

TIME	ACTIVITY DESCRIPTION	DURATION	CALORIES BURNT	DISTANCE	STEPS

Toning Exercises

EXERCISES	SETS	REPS	WEIGHT	TIME	CALORIES BURNT

DAY 10 – MY DAILY JOURNAL

What worked well?

_____
_____
_____

What didn't work well?

_____
_____
_____

I experienced the following changes:

_____
_____
_____

**Ways to overcome these challenges
(brainstorm as many problem solvers as you can):**

_____
_____
_____

**From your list choose the best solutions and develop
strategies for success.**

_____
_____
_____

Reflections: Write in your journal how you're feeling, your successes,
anything that comes to mind about your progress so far. Read through
The 17 Day Diet book to learn about all my strategies for overcoming
barriers. Which ones can you apply today?

_____
_____
_____
_____
_____

DAY 11 – MY DAILY FOOD CHART   DATE

Dr Mike's Food Tip of the Day

Get enough sleep so you don't overeat! University of Chicago researchers in the US have concluded that lack of sleep disrupts two hormones that regulate appetite – leptin, a hormone that tells the brain when it is time to eat, and ghrelin, a hormone that triggers hunger. Without enough sleep (eight hours for most of us), you may begin to crave foods high in carbohydrates, calories, fat and sugar.

WEIGHT

WATER INTAKE

number of 240-ml/
8-fl-oz glasses

☐ ☐ ☐ ☐
☐ ☐ ☐ ☐

FOOD INTAKE

number of servings

☐ Lean Proteins

☐ Cleansing
   Vegetables

☐ Natural Starch/
   High-Fibre
   Cereal/or Pasta
   (2 servings)

☐ Fruit (2 servings)

☐ Probiotic Foods/
   Dairy/Dairy Subs
   (2 servings)

☐ Friendly Fats
   (1–2 tablespoons)

☐ Optional snack

Breakfast

_____

_____

_____

_____

_____

Lunch

_____

_____

_____

_____

Dinner

_____

_____

_____

Snacks

_____

_____

Dr Mike's Workout Tip of the Day

Straighten that sedentary slump! Aerobic exercise, strength-training exercises and stretching exercises work together to improve bad posture. Aerobic exercises help back muscles to become less stiff and more flexible, whilst sit-ups, press-ups and shoulder raises, with or without weights, strengthen your back, shoulders and stomach muscles. Also try Pilates and yoga for improving posture and flexibility.

Cardio

TIME	ACTIVITY DESCRIPTION	DURATION	CALORIES BURNT	DISTANCE	STEPS

Toning Exercises

EXERCISES	SETS	REPS	WEIGHT	TIME	CALORIES BURNT

DAY 11 – MY DAILY JOURNAL

What worked well?

_____
_____
_____

What didn't work well?

_____
_____
_____

I experienced the following changes:

_____
_____
_____

Ways to overcome these challenges
(brainstorm as many problem solvers as you can):

_____
_____
_____

From your list choose the best solutions and develop
strategies for success.

_____
_____
_____

Reflections: Write in your journal how you're feeling, your successes,
anything that comes to mind about your progress so far. Read through
The 17 Day Diet book to learn about all my strategies for overcoming
barriers. Which ones can you apply today?

_____
_____
_____
_____
_____
_____

DAY 12 – MY DAILY FOOD CHART   DATE

Dr Mike's Food Tip of the Day

Need that chocolate fix? If giving up chocolate has been a challenge for you on the 17 Day Diet, now that you are on Cycle 3, chocolate can once again be part of your life! Check out the light chocolate ice cream bars in the freezer case of your supermarket. Skinny Cow and Weight Watchers frozen bars await!

WEIGHT

WATER INTAKE

number of 240-ml/
8-fl-oz glasses

☐ ☐ ☐ ☐
☐ ☐ ☐ ☐

FOOD INTAKE

number of servings

☐ Lean Proteins

☐ Cleansing
Vegetables

☐ Natural Starch/
High-Fibre
Cereal/or Pasta
(2 servings)

☐ Fruit (2 servings)

☐ Probiotic Foods/
Dairy/Dairy Subs
(2 servings)

☐ Friendly Fats
(1–2 tablespoons)

☐ Optional snack

Breakfast

_____
_____
_____
_____
_____

Lunch

_____
_____
_____
_____

Dinner

_____
_____
_____

Snacks

_____
_____

Dr Mike's Workout Tip of the Day

Have you heard the phrase 'Not exercising is not an option'? I hope by now that you feel this way and have made a commitment to daily exercise. Others may feel that exercising four to six days a week is enough to maintain a good fitness level, but I recommend a daily goal. If you commit to it, you will be less likely to make excuses to miss a day, then two and backsliding on your exercise programme.

Cardio

TIME	ACTIVITY DESCRIPTION	DURATION	CALORIES BURNT	DISTANCE	STEPS

Toning Exercises

EXERCISES	SETS	REPS	WEIGHT	TIME	CALORIES BURNT

DAY 12 – MY DAILY JOURNAL

What worked well?

_____

_____

_____

What didn't work well?

_____

_____

_____

I experienced the following changes:

_____

_____

_____

**Ways to overcome these challenges
(brainstorm as many problem solvers as you can):**

_____

_____

_____

**From your list choose the best solutions and develop
strategies for success.**

_____

_____

_____

Reflections: Write in your journal how you're feeling, your successes,
anything that comes to mind about your progress so far. Read through
The 17 Day Diet book to learn about all my strategies for overcoming
barriers. Which ones can you apply today?

_____

_____

_____

_____

_____

_____

DAY 13 – MY DAILY FOOD CHART   DATE

Dr Mike's Food Tip of the Day

Have you always been a fast eater? If so here are a couple of tips to
slow down your eating, which will allow your brain to register that you
are full: chew every bite at least 10 times. It'll help your digestion too!
Put down your fork (or spoon) between bites. This will force you to
break the 'wolf it down' syndrome.

WEIGHT

Breakfast

WATER INTAKE

number of 240-ml/
8-fl-oz glasses

☐ ☐ ☐ ☐
☐ ☐ ☐ ☐

FOOD INTAKE

number of servings

Lunch

☐ Lean Proteins

☐ Cleansing
Vegetables

☐ Natural Starch/
High-Fibre
Cereal/or Pasta
(2 servings)

Dinner

☐ Fruit (2 servings)

☐ Probiotic Foods/
Dairy/Dairy Subs
(2 servings)

☐ Friendly Fats
(1–2 tablespoons)

Snacks

☐ Optional snack

Dr Mike's Workout Tip of the Day

During Cycle 2 I extolled the virtues of using a pedometer. Lots of other fitness gadgets are also on the market that you may find helpful to reach your fitness goals. Besides the 17 Day Diet's companion exercise DVD, *The 17 Minute Workout* (order at www.the17daydiet.com), there are heart rate monitors, exercise bands, tubes, balls and a plethora of iPhone and iPod training apps. Happy fitness shopping!

Cardio

TIME	ACTIVITY DESCRIPTION	DURATION	CALORIES BURNT	DISTANCE	STEPS

Toning Exercises

EXERCISES	SETS	REPS	WEIGHT	TIME	CALORIES BURNT

DAY 13 – MY DAILY JOURNAL

What worked well?

_____
_____
_____

What didn't work well?

_____
_____
_____

I experienced the following changes:

_____
_____
_____

**Ways to overcome these challenges
(brainstorm as many problem solvers as you can):**

_____
_____
_____

**From your list choose the best solutions and develop
strategies for success.**

_____
_____
_____

Reflections: Write in your journal how you're feeling, your successes,
anything that comes to mind about your progress so far. Read through
The 17 Day Diet book to learn about all my strategies for overcoming
barriers. Which ones can you apply today?

_____
_____
_____
_____
_____

DAY 14 – MY DAILY FOOD CHART   DATE

Dr Mike's Food Tip of the Day

Here are a couple more tips to break the 'gulp and go' habit: try using chopsticks instead of a fork and spoon to eat your next meal. Between bites, take a small sip of water. Eat with others whenever possible. Make a conscious effort to participate in the conversation, which will naturally slow down your eating.

WEIGHT

WATER INTAKE

number of 240-ml/
8-fl-oz glasses

☐ ☐ ☐ ☐
☐ ☐ ☐ ☐

FOOD INTAKE

number of servings

☐ Lean Proteins

☐ Cleansing Vegetables

☐ Natural Starch/ High-Fibre Cereal/or Pasta (2 servings)

☐ Fruit (2 servings)

☐ Probiotic Foods/ Dairy/Dairy Subs (2 servings)

☐ Friendly Fats (1–2 tablespoons)

☐ Optional snack

Breakfast

_____
_____
_____
_____
_____

Lunch

_____
_____
_____
_____

Dinner

_____
_____
_____
_____

Snacks

_____
_____

Dr Mike's Workout Tip of the Day

Exercising with your pet can be beneficial for both of you! Dogs need exercise too; in fact, it's been reported that 25–40 per cent of them are overweight or obese. It's always more fun to exercise with a companion, so if you haven't already, try including your pooch next time you think of heading out for a walk.

Cardio

TIME	ACTIVITY DESCRIPTION	DURATION	CALORIES BURNT	DISTANCE	STEPS

Toning Exercises

EXERCISES	SETS	REPS	WEIGHT	TIME	CALORIES BURNT

DAY 14 – MY DAILY JOURNAL

What worked well?

_____

_____

_____

What didn't work well?

_____

_____

_____

I experienced the following changes:

_____

_____

_____

Ways to overcome these challenges
(brainstorm as many problem solvers as you can):

_____

_____

_____

From your list choose the best solutions and develop
strategies for success.

_____

_____

_____

Reflections: Write in your journal how you're feeling, your successes,
anything that comes to mind about your progress so far. Read through
The 17 Day Diet book to learn about all my strategies for overcoming
barriers. Which ones can you apply today?

_____

_____

_____

_____

_____

_____

DAY 15 – MY DAILY FOOD CHART   DATE

Dr Mike's Food Tip of the Day

Take the focus off food. Make meals more about spending quality time
with family and friends and you'll soon find mealtimes, both the regular, everyday ones and the special occasions, will resolve less around
food and more about the memories you are making around the dinner
table.

WEIGHT

WATER INTAKE

number of 240-ml/
8-fl-oz glasses

☐ ☐ ☐ ☐
☐ ☐ ☐ ☐

FOOD INTAKE

number of servings

☐ Lean Proteins

☐ Cleansing
Vegetables

☐ Natural Starch/
High-Fibre
Cereal/or Pasta
(2 servings)

☐ Fruit (2 servings)

☐ Probiotic Foods/
Dairy/Dairy Subs
(2 servings)

☐ Friendly Fats
(1–2 tablespoons)

☐ Optional snack

Breakfast

_____
_____
_____
_____
_____

Lunch

_____
_____
_____
_____

Dinner

_____
_____
_____
_____

Snacks

_____
_____

Dr Mike's Workout Tip of the Day

You have almost completed Cycle 3, so let's talk about setbacks. The best way to deal with a setback in your food or fitness goals is first to acknowledge it, then think about why it happened and what you can do to prevent it happening again. Try not to criticise yourself for missing your workout or eating that pudding, and make a fresh start tomorrow.

Cardio

TIME	ACTIVITY DESCRIPTION	DURATION	CALORIES BURNT	DISTANCE	STEPS

Toning Exercises

EXERCISES	SETS	REPS	WEIGHT	TIME	CALORIES BURNT

DAY 15 – MY DAILY JOURNAL

What worked well?

_____

_____

_____

What didn't work well?

_____

_____

_____

I experienced the following changes:

_____

_____

_____

**Ways to overcome these challenges
(brainstorm as many problem solvers as you can):**

_____

_____

_____

**From your list choose the best solutions and develop
strategies for success.**

_____

_____

_____

Reflections: Write in your journal how you're feeling, your successes,
anything that comes to mind about your progress so far. Read through
The 17 Day Diet book to learn about all my strategies for overcoming
barriers. Which ones can you apply today?

_____

_____

_____

_____

_____

_____

DAY 16 – MY DAILY FOOD CHART   DATE

Dr Mike's Food Tip of the Day

Did you used to skip a meal? Maybe you often skipped meals because you thought it would help you lose weight, or you thought you were too busy to eat. Hopefully by now you realise it's better to eat at regular intervals throughout the day to keep your metabolism elevated so your body doesn't go into starvation mode. If you used to skip meals, don't allow yourself to slip back into that harmful habit.

WEIGHT

WATER INTAKE

number of 240-ml/
8-fl-oz glasses

☐ ☐ ☐ ☐
☐ ☐ ☐ ☐

FOOD INTAKE

number of servings

☐ Lean Proteins

☐ Cleansing
Vegetables

☐ Natural Starch/
High-Fibre
Cereal/or Pasta
(2 servings)

☐ Fruit (2 servings)

☐ Probiotic Foods/
Dairy/Dairy Subs
(2 servings)

☐ Friendly Fats
(1–2 tablespoons)

☐ Optional snack

Breakfast

_____
_____
_____
_____
_____

Lunch

_____
_____
_____
_____

Dinner

_____
_____
_____
_____

Snacks

_____
_____

Dr Mike's Workout Tip of the Day

Get fit, not flabby! Weight loss can be accomplished without exercise, but those who fail to move their bodies lose weight and muscle tone at the same time. Who wants to lose pounds but be flabby? Toning muscles as weight is lost helps eliminate flab and if you have strengthened your core muscles, you will be healthier and have fewer aches and pains than those who have lost weight without working out.

Cardio

TIME	ACTIVITY DESCRIPTION	DURATION	CALORIES BURNT	DISTANCE	STEPS

Toning Exercises

EXERCISES	SETS	REPS	WEIGHT	TIME	CALORIES BURNT

DAY 16 – MY DAILY JOURNAL

What worked well?

_____
_____
_____

What didn't work well?

_____
_____
_____

I experienced the following changes:

_____
_____
_____

**Ways to overcome these challenges
(brainstorm as many problem solvers as you can):**

_____
_____
_____

**From your list choose the best solutions and develop
strategies for success.**

_____
_____
_____

Reflections: Write in your journal how you're feeling, your successes, anything that comes to mind about your progress so far. Read through *The 17 Day Diet* book to learn about all my strategies for overcoming barriers. Which ones can you apply today?

_____
_____
_____
_____
_____
_____

DAY 17 – MY DAILY FOOD CHART   DATE

Dr Mike's Food Tip of the Day

A food-mood connection has been made involving serotonin, a neurotransmitter in the brain that can affect everything from mood to metabolism and sleep to sexuality. The food connection is made because serotonin is made from tryptophan, found in lots of foods: turkey, red meat, fish and shellfish, beans, oat, nuts and seeds, to name some of them. When consumed with carbs, in particular, serotonin levels rise and mood improves too!

WEIGHT

WATER INTAKE

number of 240-ml/
8-fl-oz glasses

☐ ☐ ☐ ☐
☐ ☐ ☐ ☐

FOOD INTAKE

number of servings

☐ Lean Proteins

☐ Cleansing
Vegetables

☐ Natural Starch/
High-Fibre
Cereal/or Pasta
(2 servings)

☐ Fruit (2 servings)

☐ Probiotic Foods/
Dairy/Dairy Subs
(2 servings)

☐ Friendly Fats
(1–2 tablespoons)

☐ Optional snack

Breakfast

_____

_____

_____

_____

_____

Lunch

_____

_____

_____

_____

_____

Dinner

_____

_____

_____

_____

Snacks

_____

_____

Dr Mike's Workout Tip of the Day

Exercising with a cold can actually help speed up your recovery, so don't let a run-of-the-mill rhinovirus stop you from going for a 30 to 45-minute walk. Just leave your intense workout for another day. If you have flu symptoms, however – fever, aches, chest congestion, swollen glands – exercising can make things worse. After your fever is gone and you are symptom free, you can begin to exercise moderately.

Cardio

TIME	ACTIVITY DESCRIPTION	DURATION	CALORIES BURNT	DISTANCE	STEPS

Toning Exercises

EXERCISES	SETS	REPS	WEIGHT	TIME	CALORIES BURNT

DAY 17 – MY DAILY JOURNAL

What worked well?

_____

_____

_____

What didn't work well?

_____

_____

_____

I experienced the following changes:

_____

_____

_____

**Ways to overcome these challenges
(brainstorm as many problem solvers as you can):**

_____

_____

_____

**From your list choose the best solutions and develop
strategies for success.**

_____

_____

_____

Reflections: Write in your journal how you're feeling, your successes,
anything that comes to mind about your progress so far. Read through
The 17 Day Diet book to learn about all my strategies for overcoming
barriers. Which ones can you apply today?

_____

_____

_____

_____

_____

_____

Review: Weight Loss Checklist – Cycle 3

You've been following the 17 Day Diet for more than a month now. Are you finding any of these obstacles standing in the way of your weight loss?

1. Am I liable to overeat at certain times of day or on certain days of the week?

    ☐ **Always**   ☐ **Sometimes**   ☐ **Rarely or Never**

2. Are my portion sizes larger than they should be?

    ☐ **Always**   ☐ **Sometimes**   ☐ **Rarely or Never**

3. Am I eating while driving?

    ☐ **Always**   ☐ **Sometimes**   ☐ **Rarely or Never**

4. Am I eating at times I shouldn't, when I'm bored or stressed?

    ☐ **Always**   ☐ **Sometimes**   ☐ **Rarely or Never**

5. Am I making excuses for not working out on a daily basis?

    ☐ **Always**   ☐ **Sometimes**   ☐ **Rarely or Never**

My top areas to work on in the next cycle:

_____

_____

_____

_____

I lost _____ kg/lb on Cycle 3.

What positive new lifestyle patterns and habits are emerging in your life now? List as many as you can think of.

_____

_____

_____

_____

I have met/have not yet met my goal. Circle the one which applies.

If you have not met your goal, let's talk about what to do next. You have several choices:

- Begin with Cycle 1 and work your way back through the cycles.
- If you're very close to your goal, stay on Cycle 1 until you reach it.
- Use Cycles 2, then 3, to reach your goal.
- Stay on Cycle 3 until you reach your goal.

Which strategy will you use?

CYCLE 4

· · · · · · · · · · · · · · · ·

Arrive

GOAL:

To keep you at your goal weight through a programme of eating that lets you enjoy your favourite foods on weekends, whilst eating healthily during the week.

Start the Arrive Cycle

The Arrive Cycle is unique in that it helps you keep your weight off whilst letting you enjoy yourself and eat freely from your favourite foods on weekends.

Basically the Arrive Cycle works like this:

- Monday breakfast through Friday lunch: enjoy meal plans from one of your favourite cycles: Accelerate, Activate or Achieve.

- Friday dinner through Sunday dinner: enjoy your favourite foods and meals in moderation over the weekend.

- Enjoy no more than one to three favourite meals over the weekend. Do not binge. Eat slowly and enjoy your food.

- If desired, enjoy alcoholic drinks in moderation over the weekend (1 to 2 daily): 45 ml/1½ fl oz spirits, 150 ml/5 fl oz wine or 350 ml/12 fl oz beer.

- You may include soups in your daily menus as long as they are broth based. Avoid soups made with milk or cream. Having soup prior to a meal will help curb your appetite and help you feel full.

- As one of your fruit servings you may substitute fruit juice (unsweetened), but no more than 185 ml/6 fl oz per serving.

- Feel free to enjoy 240 ml/8 fl oz of vegetable juice as a snack.

- Continue to use condiments in moderation. Choose nonfat, low-calorie seasonings such as reduced-fat dressings, spices, herbs, lemon or lime juice, vinegar and chilli sauce.

- Exercise on weekends as well as weekdays.

- Each Monday I'd like you to renew your commitment to yourself and to your new incredible body. Do this and you'll control your eating week by week, with a strategy that'll guarantee success.

DAY 1 – MY DAILY FOOD CHART   DATE

Dr Mike's Food Tip of the Day

What foods have you missed? Fish and chips with mushy peas? Sweet and sour chicken with a spring roll? Lasagne and tiramisu? Now that you have arrived at your goal weight (applause, applause!), strategic cheating on the weekends is your reward. Enjoy up to three of your favourite meals over the weekend. Splurge a little but don't binge!

WEIGHT

WATER INTAKE

number of 240-ml/
8-fl-oz glasses

☐ ☐ ☐ ☐
☐ ☐ ☐ ☐

FOOD INTAKE

number of servings

☐ Lean Proteins

☐ Cleansing
Vegetables

☐ Natural Starch/
High-Fibre
Cereal/or Pasta
(2 servings)

☐ Fruit (2 servings)

☐ Probiotic Foods/
Dairy/Dairy Subs
(2 servings)

☐ Friendly Fats
(1–2 tablespoons)

☐ Optional snack

Breakfast

_____
_____
_____
_____
_____

Lunch

_____
_____
_____
_____
_____

Dinner

_____
_____
_____
_____

Snacks

_____
_____

Dr Mike's Workout Tip of the Day

Medically speaking, reaching your goal weight is one of the best things you have done for your health. And it's thanks in large part to leading a more active life. If appropriate, ask a health-care provider to check your blood pressure, cholesterol and blood sugar now that you have completed the first three cycles of the 17 Day Diet.

Cardio

TIME	ACTIVITY DESCRIPTION	DURATION	CALORIES BURNT	DISTANCE	STEPS

Toning Exercises

EXERCISES	SETS	REPS	WEIGHT	TIME	CALORIES BURNT

DAY 1 – MY DAILY JOURNAL

What worked well?

_____

_____

_____

What didn't work well?

_____

_____

_____

I experienced the following changes:

_____

_____

_____

**Ways to overcome these challenges
(brainstorm as many problem solvers as you can):**

_____

_____

_____

**From your list choose the best solutions and develop
strategies for success.**

_____

_____

_____

Reflections: Write in your journal how you're feeling, your successes,
anything that comes to mind about your progress so far. Read through
The 17 Day Diet book to learn about all my strategies for overcoming
barriers. Which ones can you apply today?

_____

_____

_____

_____

_____

_____

_____

DAY 2 – MY DAILY FOOD CHART   DATE

Dr Mike's Food Tip of the Day

To stay in control of portions when dining out, ask for half of your entrée to be wrapped up in a parcel before it appears on your plate. Fill up on salad, sans the croutons and cheese. Light dressing on the side, please!

WEIGHT

WATER INTAKE

number of 240-ml/
8-fl-oz glasses

☐ ☐ ☐ ☐
☐ ☐ ☐ ☐

FOOD INTAKE

number of servings

☐ Lean Proteins

☐ Cleansing
  Vegetables

☐ Natural Starch/
  High-Fibre
  Cereal/or Pasta
  (2 servings)

☐ Fruit (2 servings)

☐ Probiotic Foods/
  Dairy/Dairy Subs
  (2 servings)

☐ Friendly Fats
  (1–2 tablespoons)

☐ Optional snack

Breakfast

_____

_____

_____

_____

_____

Lunch

_____

_____

_____

_____

Dinner

_____

_____

_____

_____

Snacks

_____

_____

Dr Mike's Workout Tip of the Day

No wonder our ancestors who farmed the land could eat anything they wanted and not gain weight! Farming, baling hay and other chores can burn between 500–600 calories per hour! Maybe you're not going to drive to the country and help clean out a barn, but how about tackling that overloaded garage this weekend?

Cardio

TIME	ACTIVITY DESCRIPTION	DURATION	CALORIES BURNT	DISTANCE	STEPS

Toning Exercises

EXERCISES	SETS	REPS	WEIGHT	TIME	CALORIES BURNT

DAY 2 – MY DAILY JOURNAL

What worked well?

_____

_____

_____

What didn't work well?

_____

_____

_____

I experienced the following changes:

_____

_____

_____

Ways to overcome these challenges
(brainstorm as many problem solvers as you can):

_____

_____

_____

From your list choose the best solutions and develop
strategies for success.

_____

_____

_____

Reflections: Write in your journal how you're feeling, your successes, anything that comes to mind about your progress so far. Read through *The 17 Day Diet* book to learn about all my strategies for overcoming barriers. Which ones can you apply today?

_____

_____

_____

_____

_____

_____

DAY 3 – MY DAILY FOOD CHART   DATE

Dr Mike's Food Tip of the Day

Keeping weight off after you've lost it is made easier when you make healthier substitutes all or most of the time. You use mustard instead of mayo on sandwiches, you purchase skimmed instead of semi-skimmed or fulll-fat milk, and fat-free, sugar-free ice cream and frozen treats. Make it a mindset – a part of your lifestyle, not a diet.

WEIGHT

WATER INTAKE

number of 240-ml/
8-fl-oz glasses

☐ ☐ ☐ ☐
☐ ☐ ☐ ☐

FOOD INTAKE

number of servings

☐ Lean Proteins

☐ Cleansing
Vegetables

☐ Natural Starch/
High-Fibre
Cereal/or Pasta
(2 servings)

☐ Fruit (2 servings)

☐ Probiotic Foods/
Dairy/Dairy Subs
(2 servings)

☐ Friendly Fats
(1–2 tablespoons)

☐ Optional snack

Breakfast

_____
_____
_____
_____
_____

Lunch

_____
_____
_____
_____
_____

Dinner

_____
_____
_____
_____

Snacks

_____
_____

Dr Mike's Workout Tip of the Day

Have you thought about setting a fitness challenge for yourself, now that you are down to your goal weight? Think about signing up for the next charity walk or run in your community. You'll be helping out a worthy cause whilst helping your fine, fit self stay that way!

Cardio

TIME	ACTIVITY DESCRIPTION	DURATION	CALORIES BURNT	DISTANCE	STEPS

Toning Exercises

EXERCISES	SETS	REPS	WEIGHT	TIME	CALORIES BURNT

DAY 3 – MY DAILY JOURNAL

What worked well?

_____

_____

_____

What didn't work well?

_____

_____

_____

I experienced the following changes:

_____

_____

_____

Ways to overcome these challenges
(brainstorm as many problem solvers as you can):

_____

_____

_____

From your list choose the best solutions and develop
strategies for success.

_____

_____

_____

Reflections: Write in your journal how you're feeling, your successes,
anything that comes to mind about your progress so far. Read through
The 17 Day Diet book to learn about all my strategies for overcoming
barriers. Which ones can you apply today?

_____

_____

_____

_____

_____

_____

DAY 4 – MY DAILY FOOD CHART   DATE

Dr Mike's Food Tip of the Day

Careful! Don't pull the trigger . . . on the foods that spell trouble for you. Are potato crisps a trouble food for you? Is it hard to eat 15 crisps and stop? How about chocolate? Can you eat just three chocolates in a box and go on your way? If there are certain foods that can cause you to go into binge mode, you may have to eliminate them from your life, not just from your weekend treat meals.

WEIGHT

WATER INTAKE

number of 240-ml/
8-fl-oz glasses

☐ ☐ ☐ ☐
☐ ☐ ☐ ☐

FOOD INTAKE

number of servings

☐ Lean Proteins

☐ Cleansing
Vegetables

☐ Natural Starch/
High-Fibre
Cereal/or Pasta
(2 servings)

☐ Fruit (2 servings)

☐ Probiotic Foods/
Dairy/Dairy Subs
(2 servings)

☐ Friendly Fats
(1–2 tablespoons)

☐ Optional snack

Breakfast

Lunch

Dinner

Snacks

Dr Mike's Workout Tip of the Day

Should you let the housekeeper go? Clean your own house and you'll burn about 250 calories per hour and put extra money in your budget for, what else? A new pair of workout shoes!

Cardio

TIME	ACTIVITY DESCRIPTION	DURATION	CALORIES BURNT	DISTANCE	STEPS

Toning Exercises

EXERCISES	SETS	REPS	WEIGHT	TIME	CALORIES BURNT

DAY 4 – MY DAILY JOURNAL

What worked well?

_____
_____
_____

What didn't work well?

_____
_____
_____

I experienced the following changes:

_____
_____
_____

Ways to overcome these challenges
(brainstorm as many problem solvers as you can):

_____
_____
_____

From your list choose the best solutions and develop
strategies for success.

_____
_____
_____

Reflections: Write in your journal how you're feeling, your successes,
anything that comes to mind about your progress so far. Read through
The 17 Day Diet book to learn about all my strategies for overcoming
barriers. Which ones can you apply today?

_____
_____
_____
_____
_____
_____

DAY 5 – MY DAILY FOOD CHART   DATE

Dr Mike's Food Tip of the Day

Love your body. Change the way you dress to flatter your physique. Some clothes make you look much heavier than you are. Look for fabrics and styles that make you look thinner before you even lose a pound of fat. Change your hairstyle and if necessary, colour it. Take care of your skin. Looking better can help you follow the programme more effectively.

WEIGHT

WATER INTAKE

number of 240-ml/
8-fl-oz glasses

☐ ☐ ☐ ☐
☐ ☐ ☐ ☐

FOOD INTAKE

number of servings

☐ Lean Proteins

☐ Cleansing
Vegetables

☐ Natural Starch/
High-Fibre
Cereal/or Pasta
(2 servings)

☐ Fruit (2 servings)

☐ Probiotic Foods/
Dairy/Dairy Subs
(2 servings)

☐ Friendly Fats
(1–2 tablespoons)

☐ Optional snack

Breakfast

_____
_____
_____
_____
_____

Lunch

_____
_____
_____
_____

Dinner

_____
_____
_____

Snacks

_____
_____

Dr Mike's Workout Tip of the Day

What is your 'new normal'? Just think for a moment about how you were spending your leisure hours before the 17 Day Diet, and what has become your new normal . . . Do you recognise the couch potato that rarely walked for the sake of walking to improve your level of fitness, as well as your health? Change *can* come quickly, if you are committed to it.

Cardio

TIME	ACTIVITY DESCRIPTION	DURATION	CALORIES BURNT	DISTANCE	STEPS

Toning Exercises

EXERCISES	SETS	REPS	WEIGHT	TIME	CALORIES BURNT

DAY 5 – MY DAILY JOURNAL

What worked well?

_____
_____
_____

What didn't work well?

_____
_____
_____

I experienced the following changes:

_____
_____
_____

Ways to overcome these challenges
(brainstorm as many problem solvers as you can):

_____
_____
_____

From your list choose the best solutions and develop
strategies for success.

_____
_____
_____

Reflections: Write in your journal how you're feeling, your successes, anything that comes to mind about your progress so far. Read through *The 17 Day Diet* book to learn about all my strategies for overcoming barriers. Which ones can you apply today?

_____
_____
_____
_____
_____
_____

DAY 6 – MY DAILY FOOD CHART   DATE

Dr Mike's Food Tip of the Day

'If you always do what you always did, you'll always get what you always got.' Keep this mantra front and centre on your fridge, along with a photo of your fine-lookin' new self! You have changed the way you think about food and have seen results. You have formed new habits and have committed to a different lifestyle in less than two months. Celebrate your success!

WEIGHT

WATER INTAKE

number of 240-ml/
8-fl-oz glasses

☐ ☐ ☐ ☐
☐ ☐ ☐ ☐

FOOD INTAKE

number of servings

☐ Lean Proteins

☐ Cleansing Vegetables

☐ Natural Starch/
High-Fibre
Cereal/or Pasta
(2 servings)

☐ Fruit (2 servings)

☐ Probiotic Foods/
Dairy/Dairy Subs
(2 servings)

☐ Friendly Fats
(1–2 tablespoons)

☐ Optional snack

Breakfast

_____

_____

_____

_____

_____

Lunch

_____

_____

_____

_____

Dinner

_____

_____

_____

_____

Snacks

_____

_____

Dr Mike's Workout Tip of the Day

If you have been exercising hard during your weight loss cycles, you may find 'lifestyle activities' will be easier to fit into your daily routine. That doesn't mean you will be abandoning your workouts, whether they have included walking, jogging, swimming, aerobic dance classes, etc., but maybe the ratio will change. You have more energy and feel more like tackling those DIY projects or planting a garden.

Cardio

TIME	ACTIVITY DESCRIPTION	DURATION	CALORIES BURNT	DISTANCE	STEPS

Toning Exercises

EXERCISES	SETS	REPS	WEIGHT	TIME	CALORIES BURNT

DAY 6 – MY DAILY JOURNAL

What worked well?

_____

_____

_____

What didn't work well?

_____

_____

_____

I experienced the following changes:

_____

_____

_____

**Ways to overcome these challenges
(brainstorm as many problem solvers as you can):**

_____

_____

_____

**From your list choose the best solutions and develop
strategies for success.**

_____

_____

_____

Reflections: Write in your journal how you're feeling, your successes,
anything that comes to mind about your progress so far. Read through
The 17 Day Diet book to learn about all my strategies for overcoming
barriers. Which ones can you apply today?

_____

_____

_____

_____

_____

_____

DAY 7 – MY DAILY FOOD CHART   DATE

Dr Mike's Food Tip of the Day

It's been a time of discovery. Hopefully, during Cycles 1, 2 and 3, you were exposed to some new foods and preparation methods that you will continue to enjoy for the rest of your life. The deep-fryer was in your last car boot sale (right?) and has been replaced by low-fat, healthy ways of cooking that leave you satisfied and svelte!

WEIGHT

WATER INTAKE

number of 240-ml/
8-fl-oz glasses

☐ ☐ ☐ ☐
☐ ☐ ☐ ☐

FOOD INTAKE

number of servings

☐ Lean Proteins

☐ Cleansing
Vegetables

☐ Natural Starch/
High-Fibre
Cereal/or Pasta
(2 servings)

☐ Fruit (2 servings)

☐ Probiotic Foods/
Dairy/Dairy Subs
(2 servings)

☐ Friendly Fats
(1–2 tablespoons)

☐ Optional snack

Breakfast

_____
_____
_____
_____
_____

Lunch

_____
_____
_____
_____
_____

Dinner

_____
_____
_____
_____

Snacks

_____
_____

Dr Mike's Workout Tip of the Day

You've heard these before, but now that you are thinner and healthier, maybe you'll take them to heart: park further away from your destination and walk. Take the stairs instead of the lift. When weather permits take a walk after lunch or during your work break. Walk or ride your bike to the neighbourhood market or other locations within a mile or two of your home. Lead a fit life!

Cardio

TIME	ACTIVITY DESCRIPTION	DURATION	CALORIES BURNT	DISTANCE	STEPS

Toning Exercises

EXERCISES	SETS	REPS	WEIGHT	TIME	CALORIES BURNT

DAY 7 – MY DAILY JOURNAL

What worked well?

_____
_____
_____

What didn't work well?

_____
_____
_____

I experienced the following changes:

_____
_____
_____

**Ways to overcome these challenges
(brainstorm as many problem solvers as you can):**

_____
_____
_____

**From your list choose the best solutions and develop
strategies for success.**

_____
_____
_____

Reflections: Write in your journal how you're feeling, your successes,
anything that comes to mind about your progress so far. Read through
The 17 Day Diet book to learn about all my strategies for overcoming
barriers. Which ones can you apply today?

_____
_____
_____
_____
_____
_____

DAY 8 – MY DAILY FOOD CHART   DATE

Dr Mike's Food Tip of the Day

What are you doing to be amongst the small percentage of dieters who keep their weight off for the long term? The National Weight Control Registry, which has tracked the progress of more than American 5,000 dieters since 1994, reports that those who successfully maintain their weight loss continue to eat a low-fat diet, don't miss out on breakfast, weigh themselves regularly and exercise daily.

WEIGHT

WATER INTAKE

number of 240-ml/
8-fl-oz glasses

☐ ☐ ☐ ☐
☐ ☐ ☐ ☐

FOOD INTAKE

number of servings

☐ Lean Proteins

☐ Cleansing
   Vegetables

☐ Natural Starch/
   High-Fibre
   Cereal/or Pasta
   (2 servings)

☐ Fruit (2 servings)

☐ Probiotic Foods/
   Dairy/Dairy Subs
   (2 servings)

☐ Friendly Fats
   (1–2 tablespoons)

☐ Optional snack

Breakfast

_____
_____
_____
_____
_____

Lunch

_____
_____
_____
_____

Dinner

_____
_____
_____
_____

Snacks

_____
_____

Dr Mike's Workout Tip of the Day

Weekend chores like mowing the lawn, which burns nearly 400 calories per hour, and other garden work can help you burn those extra calories you will be consuming on your weekend 'free' days. Even getting out and watering the lawn and garden by hand burns just over 100 calories per hour, so get out and stay active!

Cardio

TIME	ACTIVITY DESCRIPTION	DURATION	CALORIES BURNT	DISTANCE	STEPS

Toning Exercises

EXERCISES	SETS	REPS	WEIGHT	TIME	CALORIES BURNT

DAY 8 – MY DAILY JOURNAL

What worked well?

_____
_____
_____

What didn't work well?

_____
_____
_____

I experienced the following changes:

_____
_____
_____

Ways to overcome these challenges
(brainstorm as many problem solvers as you can):

_____
_____
_____

From your list choose the best solutions and develop
strategies for success.

_____
_____
_____

Reflections: Write in your journal how you're feeling, your successes,
anything that comes to mind about your progress so far. Read through
The 17 Day Diet book to learn about all my strategies for overcoming
barriers. Which ones can you apply today?

_____
_____
_____
_____
_____
_____

DAY 9 – MY DAILY FOOD CHART   DATE

Dr Mike's Food Tip of the Day

'Special orders don't upset us . . .' should be the policy at any restaurant you visit, whether it's a fancy restaurant or part of a fast food chain. Don't hesitate to ask the person serving you if you can request a particular dish to be grilled or baked instead of fried, or if steamed veggies can be substituted for potato chips.

WEIGHT

WATER INTAKE

number of 240-ml/
8-fl-oz glasses

☐ ☐ ☐ ☐
☐ ☐ ☐ ☐

FOOD INTAKE

number of servings

☐ Lean Proteins

☐ Cleansing Vegetables

☐ Natural Starch/ High-Fibre Cereal/or Pasta (2 servings)

☐ Fruit (2 servings)

☐ Probiotic Foods/ Dairy/Dairy Subs (2 servings)

☐ Friendly Fats (1–2 tablespoons)

☐ Optional snack

Breakfast

_____
_____
_____
_____
_____

Lunch

_____
_____
_____
_____
_____

Dinner

_____
_____
_____
_____

Snacks

_____
_____
_____

Dr Mike's Workout Tip of the Day

Share and share alike. Have you found a fitness partner in your spouse, significant other or friend? If you haven't yet persuaded one or more of your nearest and dearest to join you in your daily workout, keep trying. Plan an outing that involves being active, like taking a nature walk. Appeal to their interests, appeal to their health and appeal to their hearts!

Cardio

TIME	ACTIVITY DESCRIPTION	DURATION	CALORIES BURNT	DISTANCE	STEPS

Toning Exercises

EXERCISES	SETS	REPS	WEIGHT	TIME	CALORIES BURNT

DAY 9 – MY DAILY JOURNAL

What worked well?

_____
_____
_____

What didn't work well?

_____
_____
_____

I experienced the following changes:

_____
_____
_____

Ways to overcome these challenges
(brainstorm as many problem solvers as you can):

_____
_____
_____

From your list choose the best solutions and develop
strategies for success.

_____
_____
_____

Reflections: Write in your journal how you're feeling, your successes,
anything that comes to mind about your progress so far. Read through
The 17 Day Diet book to learn about all my strategies for overcoming
barriers. Which ones can you apply today?

_____
_____
_____
_____
_____
_____

DAY 10 – MY DAILY FOOD CHART   DATE

Dr Mike's Food Tip of the Day

The Arrive Cycle cannot be approached as if you've reached the finish line and the race is over. You're still controlling your eating during the week, so you can splurge a bit on the weekends, speeding up your metabolism with the increased calorie intake. If you have a special occasion on a weekday and have that birthday cake and ice cream, enjoy it, but when the weekend rolls around, remember that you've already had your special dessert!

WEIGHT

WATER INTAKE

number of 240-ml/
8-fl-oz glasses

☐ ☐ ☐ ☐
☐ ☐ ☐ ☐

FOOD INTAKE

number of servings

☐ Lean Proteins

☐ Cleansing Vegetables

☐ Natural Starch/ High-Fibre Cereal/or Pasta (2 servings)

☐ Fruit (2 servings)

☐ Probiotic Foods/ Dairy/Dairy Subs (2 servings)

☐ Friendly Fats (1–2 tablespoons)

☐ Optional snack

Breakfast

_____

_____

_____

_____

Lunch

_____

_____

_____

_____

Dinner

_____

_____

_____

_____

Snacks

_____

_____

Dr Mike's Workout Tip of the Day

If airports have become your home away from home due to lots of business travel, make sure you travel light with a wheeled bag so you can make use of time you have before flights to walk the concourse. Wear your pedometer so you can keep track of your steps.

Cardio

TIME	ACTIVITY DESCRIPTION	DURATION	CALORIES BURNT	DISTANCE	STEPS

Toning Exercises

EXERCISES	SETS	REPS	WEIGHT	TIME	CALORIES BURNT

DAY 10 – MY DAILY JOURNAL

What worked well?

_____
_____
_____

What didn't work well?

_____
_____
_____

I experienced the following changes:

_____
_____
_____

**Ways to overcome these challenges
(brainstorm as many problem solvers as you can):**

_____
_____
_____

**From your list choose the best solutions and develop
strategies for success.**

_____
_____
_____

Reflections: Write in your journal how you're feeling, your successes,
anything that comes to mind about your progress so far. Read through
The 17 Day Diet book to learn about all my strategies for overcoming
barriers. Which ones can you apply today?

_____
_____
_____
_____
_____
_____

DAY 11 – MY DAILY FOOD CHART   DATE

Dr Mike's Food Tip of the Day

Salads, fresh fruits, yoghurt, turkey sandwiches and other healthy foods are readily available in airports these days, so it's up to you to seek them out. Even better, pack a lunch of your own, including healthy snacks, to eat on the plane or whilst waiting for your flight.

WEIGHT

WATER INTAKE

number of 240-ml/
8-fl-oz glasses

☐ ☐ ☐ ☐
☐ ☐ ☐ ☐

FOOD INTAKE

number of servings

☐ Lean Proteins

☐ Cleansing
Vegetables

☐ Natural Starch/
High-Fibre
Cereal/or Pasta
(2 servings)

☐ Fruit (2 servings)

☐ Probiotic Foods/
Dairy/Dairy Subs
(2 servings)

☐ Friendly Fats
(1–2 tablespoons)

☐ Optional snack

Breakfast

_____
_____
_____
_____
_____

Lunch

_____
_____
_____
_____

Dinner

_____
_____
_____
_____

Snacks

_____
_____

Dr Mike's Workout Tip of the Day

Think of ways you can make this year's holiday a more active one for you and your family. If your beach holiday has traditionally been spent under an umbrella with a stack of summer reads, read one less book so you can fit in long walks or jogs on the beach. Do some research to plan outings that will involve active exploration wherever you decide to go on holiday.

Cardio

TIME	ACTIVITY DESCRIPTION	DURATION	CALORIES BURNT	DISTANCE	STEPS

Toning Exercises

EXERCISES	SETS	REPS	WEIGHT	TIME	CALORIES BURNT

DAY 11 – MY DAILY JOURNAL

What worked well?

_____

_____

_____

What didn't work well?

_____

_____

_____

I experienced the following changes:

_____

_____

_____

**Ways to overcome these challenges
(brainstorm as many problem solvers as you can):**

_____

_____

_____

**From your list choose the best solutions and develop
strategies for success.**

_____

_____

_____

Reflections: Write in your journal how you're feeling, your successes,
anything that comes to mind about your progress so far. Read through
The 17 Day Diet book to learn about all my strategies for overcoming
barriers. Which ones can you apply today?

_____

_____

_____

_____

_____

_____

DAY 12 – MY DAILY FOOD CHART   DATE

Dr Mike's Food Tip of the Day

Cooking at home is the best way of staying on track with your eating plan, because you are in total control of the ingredients and methods used to prepare the meal. The calories you burn whilst cooking are an added benefit – up to 150 an hour!

WEIGHT

WATER INTAKE

number of 240-ml/
8-fl-oz glasses

☐ ☐ ☐ ☐
☐ ☐ ☐ ☐

FOOD INTAKE

number of servings

☐ Lean Proteins

☐ Cleansing
Vegetables

☐ Natural Starch/
High-Fibre
Cereal/or Pasta
(2 servings)

☐ Fruit (2 servings)

☐ Probiotic Foods/
Dairy/Dairy Subs
(2 servings)

☐ Friendly Fats
(1–2 tablespoons)

☐ Optional snack

Breakfast

_____
_____
_____
_____
_____

Lunch

_____
_____
_____

Dinner

_____
_____
_____

Snacks

_____
_____

Dr Mike's Workout Tip of the Day

Workout facilities in hotels are the norm these days, so pack your shoes and workout clothes when you travel. Other options are getting out of the hotel for a brisk walk or jog, or using your hotel room as your private gym. Find an exercise class on TV, bring your *17 Minute Workout* DVD (www.the17daydiet.com) or do floor exercises (sit-ups, press-ups, squats, etc.). Oh, and take the stairs instead of the lift!

Cardio

TIME	ACTIVITY DESCRIPTION	DURATION	CALORIES BURNT	DISTANCE	STEPS

Toning Exercises

EXERCISES	SETS	REPS	WEIGHT	TIME	CALORIES BURNT

DAY 12 – MY DAILY JOURNAL

What worked well?

_____
_____
_____

What didn't work well?

_____
_____
_____

I experienced the following changes:

_____
_____
_____

Ways to overcome these challenges
(brainstorm as many problem solvers as you can):

_____
_____
_____

From your list choose the best solutions and develop
strategies for success.

_____
_____
_____

Reflections: Write in your journal how you're feeling, your successes,
anything that comes to mind about your progress so far. Read through
The 17 Day Diet book to learn about all my strategies for overcoming
barriers. Which ones can you apply today?

_____
_____
_____
_____
_____
_____

DAY 13 – MY DAILY FOOD CHART   DATE

Dr Mike's Food Tip of the Day

More and more restaurants are providing calorie and nutrition information about items on their menus – even the major fast food chains.
Some have special sections of the menu devoted to low-fat, reduced-
calorie healthy choices for their dieting diners. Seek them out so you
can eat out without guilt!

WEIGHT

WATER INTAKE

number of 240-ml/
8-fl-oz glasses

☐ ☐ ☐ ☐
☐ ☐ ☐ ☐

FOOD INTAKE

number of servings

☐ Lean Proteins

☐ Cleansing
Vegetables

☐ Natural Starch/
High-Fibre
Cereal/or Pasta
(2 servings)

☐ Fruit (2 servings)

☐ Probiotic Foods/
Dairy/Dairy Subs
(2 servings)

☐ Friendly Fats
(1–2 tablespoons)

☐ Optional snack

Breakfast

_____
_____
_____
_____
_____
_____

Lunch

_____
_____
_____
_____
_____

Dinner

_____
_____
_____
_____
_____

Snacks

_____
_____

Dr Mike's Workout Tip of the Day

A family member is hospitalised. There is a death in the family. You've had surgery or sustained a serious injury. There will be situations in life that may prevent you exercising for periods of time. When the crisis has passed, start slowly. Try to get in 17 minutes of gentle exercise, just as you did when you began the 17 Day Diet. Build your time and distance a little each day. You will soon be back to where you were.

Cardio

TIME	ACTIVITY DESCRIPTION	DURATION	CALORIES BURNT	DISTANCE	STEPS

Toning Exercises

EXERCISES	SETS	REPS	WEIGHT	TIME	CALORIES BURNT

DAY 13 - MY DAILY JOURNAL

What worked well?

_____

_____

_____

What didn't work well?

_____

_____

_____

I experienced the following changes:

_____

_____

_____

Ways to overcome these challenges
(brainstorm as many problem solvers as you can):

_____

_____

_____

From your list choose the best solutions and develop
strategies for success.

_____

_____

_____

Reflections: Write in your journal how you're feeling, your successes,
anything that comes to mind about your progress so far. Read through
The 17 Day Diet book to learn about all my strategies for overcoming
barriers. Which ones can you apply today?

_____

_____

_____

_____

_____

_____

DAY 14 – MY DAILY FOOD CHART　　　　DATE

Dr Mike's Food Tip of the Day

Stop! If you step on the scales this weekend and see you have gained a few kilograms or pounds, it's time to put on the brakes. To get back to your goal weight fastest, go back to the Accelerate Cycle. To maintain top-of-mind awareness about your weight, record it every week. You've worked too hard to let 2.3 kg (5 lb) of weight gain double, then triple!

WEIGHT

WATER INTAKE

number of 240-ml/
8-fl-oz glasses

☐ ☐ ☐ ☐
☐ ☐ ☐ ☐

FOOD INTAKE

number of servings

☐ Lean Proteins

☐ Cleansing Vegetables

☐ Natural Starch/ High-Fibre Cereal/or Pasta (2 servings)

☐ Fruit (2 servings)

☐ Probiotic Foods/ Dairy/Dairy Subs (2 servings)

☐ Friendly Fats (1–2 tablespoons)

☐ Optional snack

Breakfast

Lunch

Dinner

Snacks

Dr Mike's Workout Tip of the Day

Adding strength training into your workout routine is important when it comes to staying healthy and keeping muscles strong. It is recommended that you alternate the days on which you focus on strength training and cardiovascular exercise. Working out with weights helps in weight loss and maintenance by helping to increase metabolism and burn calories, as well as tones and sculpts your muscles.

Cardio

TIME	ACTIVITY DESCRIPTION	DURATION	CALORIES BURNT	DISTANCE	STEPS

Toning Exercises

EXERCISES	SETS	REPS	WEIGHT	TIME	CALORIES BURNT

DAY 14 - MY DAILY JOURNAL

What worked well?

_____

_____

_____

What didn't work well?

_____

_____

_____

I experienced the following changes:

_____

_____

_____

Ways to overcome these challenges
(brainstorm as many problem solvers as you can):

_____

_____

_____

From your list choose the best solutions and develop
strategies for success.

_____

_____

_____

Reflections: Write in your journal how you're feeling, your successes,
anything that comes to mind about your progress so far. Read through
The 17 Day Diet book to learn about all my strategies for overcoming
barriers. Which ones can you apply today?

_____

_____

_____

_____

_____

_____

DAY 15 – MY DAILY FOOD CHART   DATE

Dr Mike's Food Tip of the Day

Restaurant menus can be overwhelming unless you mentally prepare yourself for what you will and won't order when dining out. Look for grilled or baked chicken dishes (without creamy sauces), grilled, baked or blackened fish, steamed veggies, rice, jacket potatoes or baked sweet potato, salad with a light dressing on the side and broth-based soups.

WEIGHT

WATER INTAKE

number of 240-ml/
8-fl-oz glasses

☐ ☐ ☐ ☐
☐ ☐ ☐ ☐

FOOD INTAKE

number of servings

☐ Lean Proteins

☐ Cleansing
Vegetables

☐ Natural Starch/
High-Fibre
Cereal/or Pasta
(2 servings)

☐ Fruit (2 servings)

☐ Probiotic Foods/
Dairy/Dairy Subs
(2 servings)

☐ Friendly Fats
(1–2 tablespoons)

☐ Optional snack

Breakfast

_____

_____

_____

_____

_____

Lunch

_____

_____

_____

_____

Dinner

_____

_____

_____

_____

Snacks

_____

_____

Dr Mike's Workout Tip of the Day

Be a child again! Playing with your children . . . or playing *like* a child is one way to keep moving in a different way. Have a hula hoop contest with them to see who can keep theirs going the longest. Skip down the pavement with your child. Climb the jungle gym with him or her at the playground, then try out the suspended rings. Climb a tree. You get the idea . . . It can be play time anytime you want it to be!

Cardio

TIME	ACTIVITY DESCRIPTION	DURATION	CALORIES BURNT	DISTANCE	STEPS

Toning Exercises

EXERCISES	SETS	REPS	WEIGHT	TIME	CALORIES BURNT

DAY 15 – MY DAILY JOURNAL

What worked well?

_____
_____
_____

What didn't work well?

_____
_____
_____

I experienced the following changes:

_____
_____
_____

Ways to overcome these challenges
(brainstorm as many problem solvers as you can):

_____
_____
_____

From your list choose the best solutions and develop
strategies for success.

_____
_____
_____

Reflections: Write in your journal how you're feeling, your successes, anything that comes to mind about your progress so far. Read through *The 17 Day Diet* book to learn about all my strategies for overcoming barriers. Which ones can you apply today?

_____
_____
_____
_____
_____

DAY 16 – MY DAILY FOOD CHART   DATE

Dr Mike's Food Tip of the Day

Low-fat and fat-free foods aren't always a healthy choice, since many of them are high in sugar and calories. Check the ingredients list, and be aware that ingredients are listed in the order they are present in the product. If sugar or glucose-fructose syrup is at the top of the ingredients list, it is not a healthy choice!

WEIGHT

WATER INTAKE

number of 240-ml/
8-fl-oz glasses

☐ ☐ ☐ ☐
☐ ☐ ☐ ☐

FOOD INTAKE

number of servings

☐ Lean Proteins

☐ Cleansing
Vegetables

☐ Natural Starch/
High-Fibre
Cereal/or Pasta
(2 servings)

☐ Fruit (2 servings)

☐ Probiotic Foods/
Dairy/Dairy Subs
(2 servings)

☐ Friendly Fats
(1–2 tablespoons)

☐ Optional snack

Breakfast

_____
_____
_____
_____
_____
_____

Lunch

_____
_____
_____
_____
_____

Dinner

_____
_____
_____
_____

Snacks

_____
_____

Dr Mike's Workout Tip of the Day

Tai chi, a gentle, flowing martial arts form that originated in China, may be a nice adjunct to your current fitness programme. Whilst it won't increase your aerobic fitness, studies show it can help lower blood pressure, boost the immune system, increase flexibility, strength and balance, and relieve stress. If tai chi classes aren't available in your area, look for a tai chi DVD to use at home.

Cardio

TIME	ACTIVITY DESCRIPTION	DURATION	CALORIES BURNT	DISTANCE	STEPS

Toning Exercises

EXERCISES	SETS	REPS	WEIGHT	TIME	CALORIES BURNT

DAY 16 – MY DAILY JOURNAL

What worked well?

_____
_____
_____

What didn't work well?

_____
_____
_____

I experienced the following changes:

_____
_____
_____

Ways to overcome these challenges
(brainstorm as many problem solvers as you can):

_____
_____
_____

From your list choose the best solutions and develop
strategies for success.

_____
_____
_____

Reflections: Write in your journal how you're feeling, your successes,
anything that comes to mind about your progress so far. Read through
The 17 Day Diet book to learn about all my strategies for overcoming
barriers. Which ones can you apply today?

_____
_____
_____
_____
_____
_____

DAY 17 – MY DAILY FOOD CHART   DATE

Dr Mike's Food Tip of the Day

Watching your weight and what you eat, day to day, gets easier as you settle in to the foods you'll shop for each week, the meals you'll prepare and those you'll avoid or limit to the weekends. Breathe a sigh of relief. Your new lifestyle of healthy eating and physical activity becomes a life of ease. You have indeed arrived!

WEIGHT

WATER INTAKE

number of 240-ml/
8-fl-oz glasses

☐ ☐ ☐ ☐
☐ ☐ ☐ ☐

FOOD INTAKE

number of servings

☐ Lean Proteins

☐ Cleansing Vegetables

☐ Natural Starch/ High-Fibre Cereal/or Pasta (2 servings)

☐ Fruit (2 servings)

☐ Probiotic Foods/ Dairy/Dairy Subs (2 servings)

☐ Friendly Fats (1–2 tablespoons)

☐ Optional snack

Breakfast

_____
_____
_____
_____
_____

Lunch

_____
_____
_____
_____

Dinner

_____
_____
_____
_____

Snacks

_____
_____

Dr Mike's Workout Tip of the Day

For many of you, exercise used to be a dirty word that you rarely used. Maybe you scoffed at those coming out of a gym or jogging in the neighbourhood. You deceived yourself into thinking you enjoyed your couch potato life. Now look at yourself in the mirror and smile. The race isn't fully run, and there will be stumbles and falls, but I encourage you to persevere. Walk on! Run on! Your body is thanking you . . .

Cardio

TIME	ACTIVITY DESCRIPTION	DURATION	CALORIES BURNT	DISTANCE	STEPS

Toning Exercises

EXERCISES	SETS	REPS	WEIGHT	TIME	CALORIES BURNT

DAY 17 – MY DAILY JOURNAL

What worked well?

_____

_____

_____

What didn't work well?

_____

_____

_____

I experienced the following changes:

_____

_____

_____

**Ways to overcome these challenges
(brainstorm as many problem solvers as you can):**

_____

_____

_____

**From your list choose the best solutions and develop
strategies for success.**

_____

_____

_____

Reflections: Write in your journal how you're feeling, your successes,
anything that comes to mind about your progress so far. Read through
The 17 Day Diet book to learn about all my strategies for overcoming
barriers. Which ones can you apply today?

_____

_____

_____

_____

_____

_____

Review: Weight Loss Checklist – Cycle 4

• •

Can you relate to any of these?

1. Am I struggling with maintaining portion control?

   ☐ **Always**   ☐ **Sometimes**   ☐ **Rarely or Never**

2. Do I find myself binging on my trouble foods?

   ☐ **Always**   ☐ **Sometimes**   ☐ **Rarely or Never**

3. Do I feel myself losing motivation to keep off the weight I've lost?

   ☐ **Always**   ☐ **Sometimes**   ☐ **Rarely or Never**

4. Am I fully committed to incorporating physical exercise into my daily life . . . for the rest of my life?

   ☐ **Always**   ☐ **Sometimes**   ☐ **Rarely or Never**

5. Am I completing at least 17 minutes of daily exercise?

   ☐ **Always**   ☐ **Sometimes**   ☐ **Rarely or Never**

If so list:

_____

_____

_____

_____

So far, I have lost _____ **kg/lb.**

The 17 Day Diet Maintenance Journal

Now that you have successfully reached your goal, it's time to look ahead to the rest of your life! Staying healthy, fit and within 1.4–2.3 kg (3–5 lb) of your goal weight is now your daily challenge. Take time to write in your journal (at least) weekly about how you are maintaining your weight, any changes in weight you are experiencing, good and bad habits, etc.

Identify and evaluate weight changes.

Are you weighing yourself at least weekly?　　　　☐ Yes　　☐ No

If there has been a weight gain, has it been recent or did it creep up gradually?

_____

_____

_____

_____

If your weight gain is more than 1.4–2.3 kg (3–5 lb) above goal weight, ask yourself:

Have I changed my eating patterns?　　　　☐ Yes　　☐ No

Have I changed my activity level?　　　　☐ Yes　　☐ No

If you answered 'yes', can you identify bad habits that have contributed to these changes? If so, explain:

_____

_____

_____

_____

Are there other contributing factors, i.e. illness, medication changes, pregnancy? If so, explain:

_____

_____

_____

_____

Action plan *(Check the actions you'll commit to, in order to get back on track.)*

- ☐ I will go back to Cycle 1 (Accelerate) or Cycle 2 (Activate) of the 17 Day Diet.
- ☐ I will begin recording my food intake.
- ☐ I will begin carefully policing my portions.
- ☐ I will restart or step up my physical activity.

Write in your own action:

_____

_____

_____

_____

Carefully think about answers to the following and record them under the headings below.

I do not want to regain the weight I have lost because:

1. _____

2. _____

3. _____

4. _____

I will strive daily to keep up the following healthy eating habits:

1. _____

2. _____

3. _____

4. _____

I will strive daily to keep up the following good exercise habits:

1. _____

2. _____

3. _____

4. _____

I must become more aware of the following areas of danger and self-sabotage:

1. _____

2. _____

3. _____

4. _____

The 17 Day Diet Shopping List

T he eyes are the window to the soul, but the storecupboard and fridge? The gateway to a big belly – unless you stock them with care. When you're dieting, it's especially important to stock up on nutritious foods and not waste calories on high-fat 'extras'. It all starts in the supermarket, so to make shopping easy, I've included a shopping list for the 17 Day Diet. It lists all of the important, high-nutrient foods you need for success. Grab a trolley and let's go!

The Perimeter

The outside aisles of the supermarket, known as the perimeter, are where you will find the majority of foods you'll be enjoying on the 17 Day Diet. This is where the cleansing vegetables, fruits, lean proteins (meat, poultry, fish) and dairy are usually located.

The Produce Aisle

Vegetables

Dark, Leafy Greens

Alfalfa *(Cycles 3–4)*
Beetroot greens *(Cycles 1–4)*
Chard *(Cycles 3–4)*
Dandelion greens *(Cycles 3–4)*
Kale *(Cycles 1–4)*

Mustard greens *(Cycles 3–4)*

Pak choi *(Cycles 3–4)*

Spring greens *(Cycles 1–4)*

Spinach *(Cycles 1–4)*

Turnip greens *(Cycles 1–4)*

Cruciferous Vegetables

Broccoli *(Cycles 1–4)*

Brussels sprouts *(Cycles 1–4)*

Cabbage *(Cycles 1–4)*

Cauliflower *(Cycles 1–4)*

Kohlrabi *(Cycles 3–4)*

Radishes *(Cycles 3–4)*

Sauerkraut *(Cycles 3–4) (Note: Sold in tubs in the produce section. Also sold in cans and bottles on interior aisles.)*

Roots and Tubers

Beetroots *(Cycles 3–4)*

Carrots *(Cycles 1–4)*

Jerusalem Artichoke *(Cycles 3–4)*

Parsnips *(Cycles 3–4)*

Potatoes *(Cycles 2–4)*

Swede *(Cycles 3–4)*

Sweet potatoes *(Cycles 2–4)*

Turnips *(Cycles 3–4)*

Yams *(Cycles 2–4)*

Salad Leaves

Arugula *(Cycles 1–4)*

Chicory *(Cycles 1–4)*

Coriander *(Cycles 3–4)*

Endive *(Cycles 1–4)*

Lettuce *(Cycles 1–4)*

- Cos
- Iceberg

* Little Gem
* Looseleaf

Parsley *(Cycles 1–4)*

Radicchio *(Cycles 1–4)*

Watercress *(Cycles 1–4)*

Pulses

Beans, snap *(French) (Cycles 1–4)*

Beans, snap *(yellow wax) (Cycles 3–4)*

Broad beans *(Cycles 2–4)*

Mangetout *(Cycles 3–4)*

Peas, shelled *(Cycles 2–4)*

Soya beans, fresh *(edamame) (Cycles 2–4)*

Mushrooms

Mushrooms *(Cycles 1–4)*

* Button
* Chestnut
* Portobello
* Shiitake

Summer Squash

Courgette *(Cycles 3–4)*

Marrow *(Cycles 3–4)*

Pattypan *(Cycles 3–4)*

Yellow Squash *(Cycles 3–4)*

Winter Squash

Acorn squash *(Cycles 2–4)*

Butternut squash *(Cycles 2–4)*

Hubbard squash *(Cycles 2–4)*

Pumpkin squash *(Cycles 2–4)*

Spaghetti squash *(Cycles 2–4)*

Other Vegetables

Artichokes *(Cycles 1–4)*

Artichoke hearts *(Cycles 1–4)*

Asparagus *(Cycles 1–4)*

Aubergine *(Cycles 1–4)*

Bamboo shoots *(Cycles 3–4)*

Celery *(Cycles 1–4)*

Corn *(Cycles 2–4)*

Cucumbers *(Cycles 1–4)*

Fennel *(Cycles 3–4)*

Grape vine leaves *(Cycles 3–4)*

Kelp *(and other edible seaweeds) (Cycles 3–4)*

Okra *(Cycles 1–4)*

Peppers, Chilli *(Cycles 3–4)*

- Jalapeño
- Serrano
- Ancho
- Pasilla

Peppers, sweet *(Cycles 1–4)*

- Green
- Red
- Yellow

Tomatoes *(Cycles 1–4)*

- Cherry
- Red
- Plum

Tomatillos *(Cycles 1–4)*

Alliums

Garlic *(Cycles 1–4)*

Leeks *(Cycles 1–4)*

Onions *(Cycles 1–4)*

Salad onions *(Cycles 1–4)*

Shallots *(Cycles 1–4)*

Soya-Based and Oriental Foods

Tofu

(If you are vegetarian, tofu can be one of your proteins on the 17 Day Diet.)

Tofu, firm *(Cycles 1–4)*

Tofu, soft *(Cycles 1–4)*

Tempeh *(Cycles 1–4)*

Tofu hot dogs, bacon and sausage links *(Cycles 1–4)*

- Tofu hot dogs
- Tofu bacon
- Tofu link sausage
- Tofu bulk sausage

Veggie burgers, crumbles and meatballs *(Cycles 1–4)*

- Burgers
- Crumbles
- Meatballs

Fruits

Berries

Blackberries *(Cycles 1–4)*

Blueberries *(Cycles 1–4)*

Cranberries *(Cycles 1–4)*

Currants *(Cycles 3–4)*

Gooseberries *(Cycles 1–4)*

Loganberries *(Cycles 1–4)*

Raspberries *(Cycles 1–4)*

Strawberries *(Cycles 1–4)*

Citrus Fruits

Grapefruit *(Cycles 1–4)*

Kumquats *(Cycles 3–4)*

Lemons *(Cycles 3–4)*

Limes *(Cycles 3–4)*

Oranges *(Cycles 1–4)*

Tangerines *(Cycles 3–4)*

Melons

Cantaloupe *(Cycles 3–4)*

Honeydew Melon *(Cycles 3–4)*

Watermelon *(Cycles 3–4)*

Tropical Fruits

Avocados, Hass *(Cycles 3–4)*

Bananas *(Cycles 3–4)*

Guava *(Cycles 3–4)*

Kiwi *(Cycles 3–4)*

Mango *(Cycles 3–4)*

Papaya *(Cycles 3–4)*

Pineapple *(Cycles 3–4)*

Plantains *(Cycles 3–4)*

Fruits with Stones

Apricots *(Cycles 3–4)*

Cherries *(Cycles 3–4)*

Nectarines *(Cycles 1–4)*

Peaches *(Cycles 1–4)*

Plums *(Cycles 1–4)*

Dried Fruits

Prunes *(Cycles 1–4)*

Grapes

Grapes

- Green *(Cycles 3–4)*
- Red *(Cycles 1–4)*

Other Fruits

Apples *(Cycles 1–4)*

Currants *(Cycles 3–4)*

Figs *(Cycles 3–4)*

Pears *(Cycles 1–4)*
Pomegranates *(Cycles 3–4)*
Rhubarb *(Cycles 3–4)*

Sandwich Meats

Only reduced fat versions of sandwich meats are on the 17 Day Diet plan.

Sandwich Meats

Chicken breast, roasted *(Cycles 1–4)*
Turkey breast, roasted *(Cycles 1–4)*

The Fish Counter

Fresh Fish

Warm Water Fish

Bass *(Cycles 1–4)*
Catfish *(Cycles 1–4)*
Cod *(Cycles 1–4)*
Halibut *(Cycles 1–4)*
Monkfish *(Cycles 1–4)*
Perch *(Cycles 1–4)*
Plaice *(Cycles 1–4)*
Pollack *(Cycles 1–4)*
Snapper *(Cycles 1–4)*
Tilapia *(Cycles 1–4)*

Cold Water Fish

Haddock *(Cycles 1–4)*
Herring *(Cycles 1–4)*

Mackerel *(Cycles 1–4)**

Mahi Mahi *(dolphin fish) (Cycles 1–4)*

Salmon *(Cycles 1–4)*

Sardines *(Cycles 1–4)*

Shark *(Cycles 1–4)†*

Sole *(Cycles 1–4)*

Swordfish *(Cycles 1–4)†*

Trout *(Cycles 1–4)*

Tuna *(canned albacore and yellowfin) (Cycles 1–4)**

Tuna *(Bigeye, Ahi) (Cycles 1–4)†*

Fresh Shellfish

Clams, cooked *(Cycles 2–4)*

Crabmeat, cooked *(Cycles 2–4)*

Lobster, steamed *(Cycles 2–4)*

Mussels, steamed *(Cycles 2–4)*

Oysters, raw *(Cycles 2–4)*

Scallops, raw *(Cycles 2–4)*

Prawns, cooked *(Cycles 2–4)*

Squid, raw *(Cycles 2–4)*

Prepared Fish and Shellfish

Smoked Salmon *(Cycles 1–4)*

(For other fish you can eat on The 17 Day Diet, see the Food Guide on pages 301–314.)

The Meat Department

Beef

Beef topside *(Cycles 2–4)*

---

*Fish with high levels of mercury (from 0.3 to 0.49 parts per million)
†Fish with highest levels of mercury (more than 0.5 parts per million) Sources: US Food and Drug Administration; Environmental Protection Agency

Braising steak *(Cycles 2–4)*
Lean steak mince *(Cycles 2–4)*
Rump steak *(Cycles 2–4)*
Sirloin beef *(Cycles 2–4)*
Skirt steaks *(Cycles 2–4)*

Pork

Pork chops *(Cycles 2–4)*
Pork fillet *(Cycles 2–4)*

Lamb

Lamb shoulder *(Cycles 2–4)*
Leg of lamb *(Cycles 2–4)*

Veal

Cutlets *(Cycles 2–4)*

Game

Beefalo *(Cycles 2–4)*
Buffalo *(Cycles 2–4)*
Venison *(Cycles 2–4)*

The Poultry Section

Chicken

Breast *(Cycles 1–4)*
Poussins *(Cycles 3–4)*

Turkey

Breast *(Cycles 1–4)*

Lean turkey mince *(Cycles 1–4)*

Game Birds

Ostrich *(Cycles 3–4)*
Pheasant *(Cycles 3–4)*
Quail *(Cycles 3–4)*

Sausage, Lunch Meats and Cured Poultry (Reduced Fat Only)

Lean back bacon *(Cycles 3–4)*
Turkey Italian sausage *(Cycles 3–4)*
Turkey ham *(Cycles 3–4)*
Turkey bacon *(Cycles 3–4)*

The Dairy Case

Cheese

Fresh Cheese

Mozzarella, low fat *(Cycles 3–4)*
Ricotta, low fat *(Cycles 3–4)*
Cottage cheese, low fat *(Cycles 3–4)*

Soft and Semi-soft Cheese (Low Fat Only)

Babybel Low Fat Cheese *(Cycles 3–4)*
Brie *(Cycles 3–4)*
Camembert *(Cycles 3–4)*
Edam *(Cycles 3–4)*
Feta *(Cycles 3–4)*
Goat *(Cycles 3–4)*
String cheese *(Cycles 3–4)*

Hard and Semi-hard Cheese (Low Fat Only)

Cheddar *(Cycles 3–4)*
Fontina *(Cycles 3–4)*
Parmigiana-reggiano *(Cycles 3–4)*

Dips and Salsa

Salsa *(Cycles 1–4)*

Butter, Margarine and Spreads

Cholesterol-lowering margarines *(Cycles 1–4)*

Milk

Low-fat buttermilk (1%) *(Cycles 3–4)*
Low-fat acidophilus milk *(Cycles 1–4)*
Nonfat, skimmed *(Cycles 3–4)*
Semi-skimmed *(Cycles 3–4)*

Cream

Soured Cream, fat free *(Cycles 1–4)*

Soya Milk and Other Dairy Substitutes

Unsweetened soya milk, most brands *(Cycles 3–4)*
Silk Soya milk, Organic Unsweetened *(Cycles 3–4)*
Sugar-free rice milk *(Cycles 3–4)*
Sugar-free almond milk *(Cycles 3–4)*
Sugar-free soya milk *(Cycles 3–4)*

Soya Products

Miso, reduced salt *(Cycles 1–4)*
Tempeh *(Cycles 1–4)*

Yoghurt and Other Cultured Foods

Kefir *(Cycles 1–4)*
Natural, full-fat milk, most brands *(Cycles 1–4)*

Natural, low-fat, most brands *(Cycles 1–4)*

Greek yoghurt *(0–2%) (Cycles 1–4)*

Yakult (probiotic beverage) *(Cycles 1–4)*

Eggs

Eggs *(Cycles 1–4)*

Egg whites *(Cycles 1–4)*

Egg substitutes *(Cycles 1–4)*

THE INTERIOR

The interior aisles of the supermarket contain foods that do not require refrigeration. These include prepared, canned and packaged foods, ranging from canned vegetables, fruit and soups to packets of cereals, grains and rice.

The Breakfast Foods Aisle

Cereal

Cold Cereal

All-Bran *(Cycles 3–4)*

All-Bran Bran Buds *(Cycles 3–4)*

Fibre One *(Cycles 3–4)*

Gluten-free cold cereals *(Cycles 3–4)*

Low-sugar muesli *(Cycles 3–4)*

Post 100% Bran *(Cycles 3–4)*

Hot Cereal

Oat flakes *(Cycles 2–4)*

Porridge oats, *(Cycles 2–4)*

Instant oats *(Cycles 2–4)*

Old-fashioned Oats, Quick *(Cycles 2–4)*

The Bread Aisle

Bread Products

Cracked wheat bread *(Cycles 3–4)*

Fibre-enriched bread *(Cycles 3–4)*

Gluten-free bread *(Cycles 3–4)*

Multigrain bread *(Cycles 3–4)*

Oat bran bread *(Cycles 3–4)*

Pumpernickel bread *(Cycles 3–4)*

Rye bread *(Cycles 3–4)*

Sprouted grain bread *(Cycles 3–4)*

Sugar-free bread *(Cycles 3–4)*

Wholemeal bread *(Cycles 3–4)*

Wholegrain tortilla *(Cycles 3–4)*

Wholegrain pitta bread *(Cycles 3–4)*

Wholegrain wraps *(Cycles 3–4)*

The Baking Aisle

For Cooking

These ingredients are sometimes used in my recipes in small amounts for baking and flavourings.

Bicarbonate of soda *(Cycles 1–4)*

Cocoa powder *(Cycles 1–4)*

Cornflour *(Cycles 1–4)*

Unflavoured gelatine *(Cycles 1–4)*

Sugar Substitute

Natural low-calorie sweetener *(Cycles 1–4)*

The Condiments Aisle

Salad Dressings

Fat-free dressings *(Cycles 1–4)*

Reduced calorie dressings *(Cycles 3–4)*

Reduced fat dressings *(Cycles 3–4)*

Light dressings *(Cycles 3–4)*

Salad dressings *(Cycles 3–4)*

Oils and Vinegars

Linseed oil *(Cycles 1–4)*

Olive oil *(Cycles 1–4)*

Rapeseed oil *(Cycles 3–4)*

Walnut oil *(Cycles 3–4)*

Balsamic vinegar *(Cycles 1–4)*

Cider vinegar *(Cycles 1–4)*

Rice vinegar *(Cycles 1–4)*

Wine vinegar *(Cycles 1–4)*

Seasoned rice vinegar *(Cycles 1–4)*

Mayonnaise

Mayonnaise, fat-free *(Cycles 1–4)*

Mayonnaise, light *(Cycles 3–4)*

Mayonnaise *(Cycles 3–4)*

Tartar Sauce

Tartar sauce, low fat *(Cycles 3–4)*

Mexican Condiments and Sauces

Salsa *(Cycles 1–4)*

Enchilada sauce *(Cycles 1–4)*

Taco sauce *(Cycles 1–4)*

Asian Condiments and Sauces

Soy sauce, light *(Cycles 1–4)*
Teriyaki sauce *(Cycles 1–4)*
Wasabi, most brands *(Cycles 1–4)*
Kimchi (Korean cabbage) *(Cycles 1–4)*

Other Condiments

Barbeque Sauce *(Cycles 1–4)*
Cocktail sauce *(Cycles 1–4)*
Clam juice *(Cycles 1–4)*
  • Clam juice, most brands
Horseradish *(Cycles 1–4)*
Hot sauce *(Cycles 1–4)*
  • Hot sauce, most brands
  • Tabasco sauce
Jams, jellies and preserves *(Cycles 1–4)*
  • No added sugar
Mustard *(Cycles 1–4)*
  • Dijon
  • Wholegrain
  • English
Pancake and Flavoured Syrups *(Cycles 1–4)*
  • Sugar free
Steak sauce *(Cycles 1–4)*
  • A1, original
Sweet relish, sugar free *(Cycles 1–4)*
Tomato ketchup *(Cycles 1–4)*
  • Reduced sugar
Worcestershire sauce *(Cycles 1–4)*

The Canned and Bottled Foods Aisle

Canned and Bottled Beans and Pulses

Aduki beans, most brands *(Cycles 2–4)*

Black beans, most brands *(Cycles 2–4)*

Black-eyed beans, most brands *(Cycles 2–4)*

Black soya beans *(Cycles 2–4)*

Butter beans, most brands *(Cycles 2–4)*

Cannellini, most brands *(Cycles 2–4)*

Chickpeas, most brands *(Cycles 2–4)*

Green split peas, most brands *(Cycles 2–4)*

Kidney beans, most brands *(Cycles 2–4)*

Lentils, most brands *(Cycles 2–4)*

Peas, most brands *(Cycles 2–4)*

Pinto beans, most brands *(Cycles 2–4)*

Red lentils, most brands *(Cycles 2–4)*

Soya beans, most brands *(Cycles 2–4)*

White beans, most brands *(Cycles 2–4)*

Canned and Bottled Soups and Broth

Chicken broth *(Cycles 1–4)*
  * Fat-free chicken broth
Beef broth *(Cycles 1–4)*
  * Fat-free beef broth
Vegetable broth *(Cycles 1–4)*
  * Fat-free vegetable broth

Canned and Bottled Vegetables

Beetroots *(Cycles 3–4)*

Cut French beans *(Cycles 1–4)*

Pineapple, canned in its own juice *(Cycles 3–4)*

Sauerkraut, canned or bottled *(Cycles 3–4)*

Canned Seafood

Baby clams *(Cycles 2–4)*

Clams, chopped or minced *(Cycles 2–4)*

Crabmeat, fancy white *(Cycles 2–4)*

Crabmeat, lump *(Cycles 2–4)*

Mackerel, most brands *(Cycles 2–4)*

Mussels, smoked *(Cycles 2–4)*

Oysters, smoked *(Cycles 2–4)*

Prawns, tiny *(Cycles 2–4)*

Prawns, medium *(Cycles 2–4)*

Salmon, all varieties, most brands *(Cycles 1–4)*

Sardines, in tomato sauce *(Cycles 1–4)*

Sardines, in water *(Cycles 1–4)*

Tuna, albacore (in water) *(Cycles 1–4)*

Tuna, chunk (in water) *(Cycles 1–4)*

Tuna, light (in water) *(Cycles 1–4)*

Canned and Bottled Tomatoes

Tomatoes, chopped *(Cycles 1–4)*

Tomatoes, crushed, with Italian herbs *(Cycles 1–4)*

Tomatoes, diced *(Cycles 1–4)*

Tomatoes, passata *(Cycles 1–4)*

Tomatoes, whole *(Cycles 1–4)*

Canned and Bottled Tomato and Pasta Sauces/ Tomato Purée

Pasta sauce, no sugar added *(Cycles 1–4)*

Tomato purée *(Cycles 1–4)*

The Pasta, Grains, Beans and Pulses Aisle

Whole Grains

Amaranth *(Cycles 2–4)*

Barley, pearl *(Cycles 2–4)*

Buckwheat groats *(kasha) (Cycles 2–4)*

Bulgar wheat *(Cycles 2–4)*

Couscous, whole wheat *(Cycles 2–4)*

Millet *(Cycles 2–4)*

Oats *(Cycles 2–4)*

Rice, brown *(Cycles 2–4)*

Rice, long grain *(basmati) (Cycles 2–4)*

Rice, wild *(Cycles 2–4)*

Dried Beans and Pulses

Aduki *(Cycles 2–4)*

Black beans *(Cycles 2–4)*

Black-eyed beans *(Cycles 2–4)*

Borlotti beans *(Roman) (Cycles 2–4)*

Broad beans *(Cycles 2–4)*

Butter beans *(Cycles 2–4)*

Cannellini *(white kidney beans) (Cycles 2–4)*

Chickpeas *(Cycles 2–4)*

Flageolet beans *(Cycles 2–4)*

Haricot beans *(Cycles 2–4)*

Lentils *(Cycles 2–4)*

Pinto beans *(Cycles 2–4)*

Red Kidney beans *(Cycles 2–4)*

Soya beans *(Cycles 2–4)*

Split peas *(Cycles 2–4)*

Pasta

Gluten-free pasta *(Cycles 3–4)*
High-fibre pasta *(Cycles 3–4)*
Soba noodles *(Cycles 3–4)*
Vegetable-based pasta *(Cycles 3–4)*
Whole-wheat pasta *(Cycles 3–4)*
- Angel hair
- Bow tie
- Penne
- Radiatori
- Shells
- Spaghetti
- Spirals

Whole-wheat spinach egg noodles *(Cycles 3–4)*
Udon noodles *(Cycles 3–4)*

The Snacks Aisle

Gelatine Mixes

Jelly mixes, all flavours *(Cycles 1–4)*

Custards

- Instant, sugar free, fat free, *(Cycles 2–4)*?
- Pudding cup, sugar free *(Cycles 3–4)*

Savoury Snacks

Popcorn, microwave, light *(Cycles 3–4)*

Nuts and Seeds

Almonds, roasted, salted *(Cycles 3–4)*

Brazil nuts *(Cycles 3–4)*

Cashews *(Cycles 3–4)*

Hazelnuts *(Cycles 3–4)*

Macadamia nuts, roasted, salted *(Cycles 3–4)*

Mixed nuts *(Cycles 3–4)*

Peanuts, cocktail *(Cycles 3–4)*

Peanuts, dry roasted *(Cycles 3–4)*

Pecans *(Cycles 3–4)*

Pine nuts *(Cycles 3–4)*

Pistachios, dry roasted, salted in shell *(Cycles 3–4)*

Pumpkin seeds *(Cycles 3–4)*

Soybean nuts *(Cycles 3–4)*

Sunflower seeds, roasted, salted *(Cycles 3–4)*

Walnuts *(Cycles 3–4)*

The Beverage Aisle

Hot Drinks

Decaf coffee *(Cycles 1–4)*

Decaf black tea *(Cycles 1–4)*

Herbal tea *(Cycles 1–4)*

Green tea *(Cycles 1–4)*

The Frozen Foods Aisle

Vegetables

Broad beans, most brands *(Cycles 2–4)*

Broccoli, most brands *(Cycles 1–4)*

Brussels sprouts, most brands *(Cycles 1–4)*

Butter beans, most brands *(Cycles 3–4)*

Cabbage, most brands *(Cycles 1–4)*

Carrots, most brands *(Cycles 1–4)*

Cauliflower, most brands *(Cycles 1–4)*

French beans, most brands *(Cycles 1–4)*

Mixed vegetables, broccoli, sweetcorn and peas *(Cycles 2–4)*

Mixed vegetables, carrots, cauliflower and peas *(Cycles 2–4)*

Kale, most brands *(Cycles 1–4)*

Okra, most brands *(Cycles 1–4)*

Parsnips, most brands *(Cycles 1–4)*

Peas, petits pois, most brands *(Cycles 2–4)*

Peas, garden, most brands *(Cycles 2–4)*

Soya beans, most brands *(Cycles 2–4)*

Spinach, most brands *(Cycles 1–4)*

Spring greens, most brands *(Cycles 1–4)*

Stir-fry vegetables, most brands *(Cycles 2–4)*

Swede, most brands *(Cycles 3–4)*

Sweetcorn, most brands *(Cycles 3–4)*

Fruits

Blackberries, most brands, unsweetened *(Cycles 1–4)*

Blueberries, most brands, unsweetened *(Cycles 1–4)*

Mixed berries, most brands, unsweetened *(Cycles 1–4)*

Mixed fruits, most brands, unsweetened *(Cycles 3–4)*

Papaya chunks, most brands, unsweetened *(Cycles 3–4)*

Peaches, most brands, unsweetened *(Cycles 1–4)*

Raspberries, most brands, unsweetened *(Cycles 1–4)*

Strawberries, sliced, most brands, unsweetened *(Cycles 1–4)*

Strawberries, whole, most brands, unsweetened *(Cycles 1–4)*

Ice Cream and Desserts

No-sugar-added ice cream, most flavours *(Cycles 3–4)*

No-sugar-added Fruit Lollies, all flavours *(Cycles 3–4)*

Skinny Cow ice cream *(Cycles 3–4)*

Frozen Dessert Novelties

Freedom frozen desserts, all flavours *(Cycles 3–4)*
Frozen yoghurt, all flavours *(Cycles 3–4)*
Swedish Glace non-dairy ice cream *(Cycles 3–4)*

17 Brand-New Recipes from Dr Mike

Smoothies

Peachy Shake

>   240 ml/8 fl oz almond milk
>   250 g/9 oz frozen peaches
>   20 g/¾ oz instant porridge oats

With the addition of oats, this shake makes a delicious, complete meal. Place all ingredients in a blender and blend until smooth. Use in Cycles 3–4.

Makes 1 serving.

Piña Colada Shake

>   125 g/4½ oz silken tofu
>   240 ml/8 fl oz almond milk
>   125 g/4½ oz crushed pineapple
>   ½ frozen banana
>   2 packets natural low-calorie sweetener
>   ½ teaspoon coconut essence

Place all ingredients in a blender and blend until smooth. Use in Cycles 3–4.

Makes 1 large serving.

Snacks, Sides and Salads

Yummus

320 g/11¼ oz cooked peas, drained
60 ml/2 fl oz water
1 teaspoon crushed garlic
1 small onion, roughly chopped
1 tablespoon olive oil
1 tablespoon lemon juice
50 g/1¾ oz Parmigiana-reggiano cheese, grated
½ teaspoon kosher salt
½ teaspoon black pepper

Place all ingredients in a blender. Pulse until mixture is smooth but not puréed. Add a little bit more water if needed. Transfer to a serving bowl. Serve with fresh diced veggies. Use in Cycles 2–4.

Yield: 4 servings

Yoghurt Cheese

900 g/2 lb fat-free Greek-style yoghurt
Spices (kosher salt, garlic powder, oregano)

Line a sieve with a coffee filter or white kitchen paper. Place the sieve over a bowl to catch the liquid. Spoon in the fat-free yoghurt. Cover and refrigerate for 8 hours or overnight. Makes about 450 g/1 lb of yoghurt cheese. Mix in your favourite spices for a tangy dip for vegetables or as a topping for jacket potatoes. Use in Cycles 1–4.

Yield: 5 servings

French Bean Casserole

> 305 g/10¾ oz canned low-fat condensed cream of
>   mushroom soup
> 60 ml/2 fl oz semi-skimmed milk
> 1 teaspoon soy sauce
> ¼ teaspoon fresh ground pepper
> 820 g/1 lb 13 oz canned French beans, drained
> 1 rasher lean back bacon, cooked and chopped
> 1 medium onion, chopped
> 1 tablespoon olive oil

In a 1½-litre (1½-quart) casserole dish, combine the soup, milk, soy sauce and pepper. Mix well. Add the beans, then sprinkle the chopped bacon over the casserole.

In a small saucepan, cook the onion in olive oil over a high heat, until the onion has browned. Place browned onions over the top of the casserole.

Bake at Gas Mark 4/180°C/fan assist 160°C for 25 minutes. Use in Cycles 1–4.

Yield: 4 servings

Leek and Tomato Soup

> 2 tablespoons olive oil
> 3 medium leeks, sliced up to the green parts
> 1 tablespoon minced garlic
> ½ teaspoon salt
> 400 g/14 oz can diced tomatoes
> 3 cups vegetable juice (V8)
> 1 teaspoon dried marjoram
> ¼ teaspoon fresh ground pepper

Heat oil in a large soup pot. Sauté leeks, garlic, and salt until leeks are soft. Slowly stir in tomatoes, tomato juice, marjoram, and pepper. Cover and cook on low heat for 20 minutes. Use in Cycles 1–4.

Yield: 4 servings

17 Day Slimming Soup

> 270 g/9½ oz cabbage, chopped
> 2 yellow squashes, chopped
> 1 large onion, chopped
> 3 large celery sticks with leaves, chopped
> 850 g/1 lb 14 oz canned crushed tomatoes
> 1.25 kg/2 lb 12 oz canned fat-free chicken broth
> 240 ml/8 fl oz vegetable juice
> 3 teaspoons salt
> ¼ teaspoon pepper

Place all ingredients in a large pot and simmer for one hour, or until the vegetables are soft. Use in Cycles 1–4.

Yield: 16 servings

Ambrosia

> 550 g/1 lb 4 oz canned crushed pineapple in 100%
>   pineapple juice
> 235 g/8¼ oz canned light fruit cocktail in pear juice,
>   drained
> 30 g/1 oz packet instant sugar-free, fat-free pistachio
>   pudding mix or another flavour of your choice
> 1 tablespoon lemon juice
> 90 g/3¼ oz sugar-free or fat-free whipped topping

Pour the pineapple with its juice into a large bowl. Stir in the drained fruit cocktail and mix well. Stir in the powdered pudding mix and blend well. Fold in the lemon juice and whipped topping and blend well. Refrigerate for at least 4 hours prior to serving. Use in Cycles 3–4.

Yield: 8 servings

Main Meals

Oven-Fried Cajun Tilapia

4 fresh tilapia fillets, 450 g/1 lb in total
90 g/3¼ oz fresh wholemeal breadcrumbs
1 teaspoon Cajun seasoning
½ teaspoon kosher salt
350 ml/12 fl oz low-fat buttermilk
Vegetable cooking spray

Spread the breadcrumbs out on a large plate. Sprinkle with the Cajun seasoning and salt. Distribute the spices evenly amongst breadcrumbs. Fill a shallow bowl with the buttermilk. Dip each fillet in the buttermilk, then coat the fillet with breadcrumbs. Place the coated fillets in a baking tin or baking tray coated with vegetable cooking spray. Then spray each fillet with the vegetable cooking spray. Bake in a preheated Gas Mark 6/200°C/fan assist 180°C oven for 10–12 minutes or until the fish flakes easily with a fork. Do not overcook. Use in Cycles 3–4.

Yield: 4 servings

Meat and Rice Loaf

205 g/7¼ oz cooked brown and wild rice
450 g/1 lb extra lean steak mince
1 egg, beaten
1 medium onion, chopped
1 teaspoon salt
¼ teaspoon garlic powder
½ teaspoon dry mustard
½ teaspoon ground sage
1 tablespoon Worcestershire sauce

Mix all ingredients together and form into a loaf. Bake at Gas Mark 4/180°C/fan assist 160°C for an hour and a half. Use in Cycles 2–4.

Yield: 4 servings

BBQ Chicken

> 4 chicken breasts
> 240 ml/8 fl oz fat-free French salad dressing
> 2 tablespoons teriyaki sauce
> 2 tablespoons light soy sauce
> 1 tablespoon carb-free barbecue sauce

To make the marinade, combine the salad dressing, teriyaki sauce, light soy sauce and barbecue sauce. Pour over the chicken breasts and let marinade for at least 3 hours in the refrigerator. Grill or bake the chicken breasts to desired doneness, basting occasionally with marinade. Use in Cycles 1–4.

Yield: 4 servings.

Herby Pork Chops

> 4 lean pork chops, about 115–140 g/4–5 oz each, all visible
>   fat trimmed
> 2 sprigs fresh rosemary (chopped leaves)
> 1 tablespoon finely chopped garlic
> 2 tablespoons olive oil

Sauté the rosemary and garlic in olive oil over a medium-low heat until the spices are soft. Add the pork chops. Cook well on both sides, Salt lightly before serving. Use in Cycles 1–4.

Yield: 4 servings

Scallops Kebab

> 450 g/1 lb raw scallops
> 1 medium red pepper
> 1 medium green pepper
> 1 medium yellow pepper
> 8 white baby onions
> 125 ml/4 fl oz fat-free Italian salad dressing

Cut the peppers into large chunks. Arrange the scallops, pepper chunks and onions on kebab skewers. Baste with vinaigrette and grill over a medium flame for about 20 minutes, brushing with remaining dressing. (A vinaigrette can be used in place of the Italian dressing.) Use in Cycles 1–4.

Yield: 4 servings

Super Stuffed Red Peppers

    4 large red peppers
    450 g/1 lb turkey mince
    1 medium onion, chopped
    2 medium tomatoes, chopped
    60 g/2¼ oz pecan nuts, chopped
    70 g/2½ oz shiitake mushrooms, chopped
    185 g/6½ oz cooked bulgar wheat
    1 tablespoon fresh basil
    1 teaspoon chilli pepper flakes
    1 teaspoon kosher salt
    ¼ teaspoon black pepper

Cut off the tops of the red peppers and deseed. Boil the peppers in a large saucepan of water until just tender. Drain on kitchen paper.

Brown the turkey in a frying pan, then drain off any fat. Add the onion, tomatoes, pecans, mushrooms, wheat and spices. Sauté until all the vegetables are soft. Stuff peppers with the mixture and bake at Gas Mark 4/180°C/fan assist 160°C for 30 minutes. Use in Cycles 3–4.

Yield: 4 servings

Mexican Bean Stew

    2 tablespoons olive oil
    3 garlic cloves, chopped
    1 medium onion, chopped
    1 green pepper, chopped
    850 g/1 lb 14 oz canned kidney beans, drained
    425 g/15 oz canned sweetcorn, drained

115 g/4 oz canned green chillies

1.6 kg/3 lb 8 oz canned crushed tomatoes

1 packet taco seasoning mix

In a large saucepan, sauté the garlic, onion and green pepper in the olive oil until tender. Add the rest of the ingredients and bring to a simmer. With the lid on, simmer for 20 minutes. Use in Cycles 3–4.

Yield: 4 servings

Frozen Treats

Super-Strawberry Frozen Yoghurt

350 g/12 oz fat-free strawberry yoghurt

2 tablespoons sugar-free strawberry jam

Mix together the yoghurt and jam. Blend well. Refrigerate for a few hours until the mixture is very cold. Pour the mixture into the freezer bowl of an ice cream maker and follow the manufacturer's instructions to freeze.

Yield: 2 servings

Chocolaty Frozen Yoghurt

350 g/12 oz low-fat Greek-style yoghurt

1 tablespoon low-fat buttermilk

1 tablespoon agave nectar

2 teaspoons cocoa powder

4 tablespoons sugar-free hot cocoa mix

½ teaspoon instant espresso powder

½ teaspoon vanilla extract

Combine the above ingredients. Mix well using a whisk. Refrigerate for a few hours until mixture is very cold. Pour the mixture into the freezer bowl of an ice cream maker and follow the manufacturer's instructions to freeze.

Yield: 2 servings

Exercise, Sports and
Everyday Activities Chart

• •

Y ou're burning calories reading this, even if you're not huffing
through a treadmill workout at the same time. Stand up and
read, and you'll fry even more calories. The point is, there's a
lot of calorie-burning activity in any kind of motion, even sex. And
the more calories you burn during the day, the more fat you lose.
To give you a comprehensive look at which activities will torch the
most calories, the chart below is adapted from the American College
of Sports Medicine's *ACM's Resource Manual for Guidelines for Exercise
Testing and Prescription.*

    To increase the rate of your calorie burning, look for ways to
increase movement in your daily routine. This chart can help you.
Also use it to log your calorie-burning in this journal.

Calories burnt per hour (for people of varying body weights)

EXERCISE	59 kg/ 130 lb	70 kg/ 155 lb	81.6 kg/ 180 lb	93 kg/ 205 lb
Aerobics, low impact	295	352	409	465
Aerobics, high impact	413	493	572	651
Aerobics, step aerobics	502	598	695	791
Aerobics, general	384	457	531	605
Aerobics class, instructing	354	422	490	558
Ballet, jazz, tap	266	317	368	419
Ballroom dancing, slow	177	211	245	279
Ballroom dancing, fast	325	387	449	512
Calisthenics, vigorous, press-ups, sit-ups	472	563	654	745
Calisthenics, light	207	246	286	326
Circuit training, minimal rest	472	563	654	745
Cycling, mountain bike, BMX	502	598	695	791
Cycling, <10 mph, leisure bicycling	236	281	327	372
Cycling, 10–11.9 mph, light	354	422	490	558
Cycling, 12–13.9 mph, moderate	472	563	654	745
Cycling, 14–15.9 mph, vigorous	590	704	817	931
Cycling, >20 mph, racing	944	1126	1308	1489
Jazzercise	354	422	490	558
Martial arts, judo, karate, jujitsu	590	704	817	931
Martial arts, kickboxing	590	704	817	931
Martial arts, tae kwon do	590	704	817	931
Rowing machine, light	207	246	286	326
Rowing machine, moderate	413	493	572	651
Rowing machine, vigorous	502	598	695	791
Running, 5 mph (12 minute mile)	472	563	654	745
Running, 5.2 mph (11.5 minute mile)	531	633	735	838
Running, 6 mph (10 minute mile)	590	704	817	931
Running, 6.7 mph (9 minute mile)	649	774	899	1024
Running, general	472	563	654	745
Ski machine	413	493	572	651
Skipping rope, fast	708	844	981	1117
Skipping rope, moderate	590	704	817	931
Skipping rope, slow	472	563	654	745
Stair machine	531	633	735	838
Stationary cycling, very light	177	211	245	279
Stationary cycling, light	325	387	449	512
Stationary cycling, moderate	413	493	572	651
Stationary cycling, vigorous	620	739	858	977
Swimming laps, freestyle, fast	590	704	817	931

EXERCISE (cont.)	59 kg/ 130 lb	70 kg/ 155 lb	81.6 kg/ 180 lb	93 kg/ 205 lb
Swimming laps, freestyle, slow	413	493	572	651
Swimming backstroke	413	493	572	651
Swimming breaststroke	590	704	817	931
Swimming butterfly	649	774	899	1024
Swimming leisurely, not laps	354	422	490	558
Swimming sidestroke	472	563	654	745
Walking, under 2.0 mph, very slow	118	141	163	186
Walking 2.0 mph, slow	148	176	204	233
Walking 2.5 mph	177	211	245	279
Walking 3.0 mph, moderate	195	232	270	307
Walking 3.5 mph, brisk pace	224	267	311	354
Walking 3.5 mph, uphill	354	422	490	558
Water aerobics	236	281	327	372
Water jogging	472	563	654	745
Weight lifting, body building, vigorous	354	422	490	558
Weight lifting, light workout	177	211	245	279
Yoga	236	281	327	372
SPORTS	59 kg/ 130 lb	70 kg/ 155 lb	81.6 kg/ 180 lb	93 kg/ 205 lb
Archery	207	246	286	326
Backpacking, walking with pack	413	493	572	651
Badminton	266	317	368	419
Basketball game, competitive	472	563	654	745
Playing basketball, non game	354	422	490	558
Billiards	148	176	204	233
Bowling	177	211	245	279
Boxing, punching bag	354	422	490	558
Boxing, sparring	531	633	735	838
Canoeing, camping trip	236	281	327	372
Canoeing, rowing, light	177	211	245	279
Canoeing, rowing, moderate	413	493	572	651
Canoeing, rowing, vigorous	708	844	981	1117
Croquet	148	176	204	233
Cross-country skiing, slow	413	493	572	651
Cross-country skiing, moderate	472	563	654	745
Cross-country skiing, vigorous	531	633	735	838
Darts (wall or lawn)	148	176	204	233
Downhill skiing, light	295	352	409	465
Downhill skiing, moderate	354	422	490	558
Downhill skiing, racing	472	563	654	745
Fencing	354	422	490	558

SPORTS (cont.)	59 kg/ 130 lb	70 kg/ 155 lb	81.6 kg/ 180 lb	93 kg/ 205 lb
Football, American	472	563	654	745
Frisbee playing, general	177	211	245	279
Golf, general	266	317	368	419
Golf, walking and carrying clubs	266	317	368	419
Golf, driving range	177	211	245	279
Golf, miniature golf	177	211	245	279
Golf, walking and pulling clubs	254	303	351	400
Golf, using power cart	207	246	286	326
Hacky sack	236	281	327	372
Handball	708	844	981	1117
Ice skating, average speed	413	493	572	651
Kayaking	295	352	409	465
Orienteering	531	633	735	838
Playing racquetball	413	493	572	651
Race walking	384	457	531	605
Riding a horse, general	236	281	327	372
Rock climbing, mountain climbing	472	563	654	745
Roller skating	413	493	572	651
Rollerblading, in-line skating	708	844	981	1117
Sailing, yachting, ocean sailing	177	211	245	279
Shuffleboard, lawn bowling	177	211	245	279
Skateboarding	295	352	409	465
Skiing, water-skiing	354	422	490	558
Ski mobiling	413	493	572	651
Skin diving, scuba diving	413	493	572	651
Sledging, tobagganing, luge	413	493	572	651
Snorkelling	295	352	409	465
Snowmobiling	207	246	286	326
Snowshoeing	472	563	654	745
Surfing, body surfing or board surfing	177	211	245	279
Softball or baseball	295	352	409	465
Squash	708	844	981	1117
Table tennis	236	281	327	372
Tai chi	236	281	327	372
Tennis, doubles	354	422	490	558
Tennis, singles	472	563	654	745
Track and field (hurdles)	590	704	817	931
Trampoline	207	246	286	326
Trekking, cross country	354	422	490	588
Volleyball, regular	177	211	245	279

SPORTS (cont.)	59 kg/ 130 lb	70 kg/ 155 lb	81.6 kg/ 180 lb	93 kg/ 205 lb
Volleyball, beach	472	563	654	745
Windsurfing, sailing	177	211	245	279
Whitewater rafting, kayaking, canoeing	295	352	409	465
EVERYDAY ACTIVITIES	59 kg/ 130 lb	70 kg/ 155 lb	81.6 kg/ 180 lb	93 kg/ 205 lb
Bird watching	148	176	204	233
General housework	207	246	286	326
Cleaning gutters	295	352	409	465
Painting	266	317	368	419
Mowing lawn, walk, power mower	325	387	449	512
Mowing lawn, riding mower	148	176	204	233
Walking, snowblower	207	246	286	326
Riding, snowblower	177	211	245	279
Sex, foreplay	86	102	119	135
Sex, intercourse	250	298	346	394
Shovelling snow by hand	354	422	490	558
Raking lawn	254	303	351	400
Gardening, general	236	281	327	372
Standing, playing with children, light	165	197	229	261
Walking the dog	177	211	245	279
Walk/run, playing with children, moderate	236	281	327	372
Walk/run, playing with children, vigorous	295	352	409	465

The 17 Day Diet Food Guide

M y Food Guide lists foods in alphabetical order so you'll have no trouble finding whatever you want to look up. Let's say, for example, you're looking for carrots. Go down to the C foods, and you'll find carrots listed there.

Each food entry lists the following information in this order: food item, serving size, calories and the amount of each of the following in grams: total fat, protein, carbohydrates and fibre. The last column designates the cycle on which you can eat the particular food.

This guide, derived from the USDA National Nutrient Database, provides you with information to help you make the best possible food choices and take steps towards reducing your weight and increasing your health. Refer to it often.

Food Item	Serving Size	Calories	Fat	Protein	Carbs	Fibre	Cycle
A							
Alfalfa sprouts	35 g/1¼ oz	10	0	0	2	0	3–4
Almond milk	240 ml/8 fl oz	60	2.5	1	8	1	3–4
Almonds, roasted	30 g/1 oz (12 nuts)	169	15	6	6	6	3–4
Amaranth	100 g/3¾ oz	360	6	14	62	14	2–4
Apples, with skin	1 medium	72	0	0	19	3	1–4
Apricots	1 apricot	17	0	0	4	1	3–4
Artichokes	1 artichoke	76	0	5	17	9	1–4
Artichoke hearts	2 pieces	30	0	1	7	2	1–4
Asparagus	1 spear	2	0	0	1	0	1–4
Aubergine	1 aubergine	110	10	5	26	16	1–4
Avocados	¼ fruit	136	12.5	2	7	6	3–4

Food Item	Serving Size	Calories	Fat	Protein	Carbs	Fibre	Cycle
B							
Bacon, lean back	1 rasher	43	2	6	0	0	2–4
Bamboo shoots, raw	150 g/5½ oz	41	1	4	8	3	3–4
Bananas	1 medium, 120 g/4½ oz	105	0	1	27	3	3–4
Barley, pearl, cooked	80 g/2¾ oz	97	0	2	22	3	2–4
Beans, aduki, cooked	115 g/4 oz	147	0	8	14	4	2–4
Beans, black, cooked	85 g/3 oz	113	0	7	20	7	2–4
Beans, borlotti, cooked	90 g/3¼ oz	120	0	8	21	9	2–4
Beans, broad, canned	125 g/4½ oz	91	0	7	15	5	2–4
Beans, butter, cooked	90 g/3¼ oz	108	0	7	20	7	2–4
Beans, butter, canned	120 g/4¼ oz	95	0	6	18	5	2–4
Beans, French, cooked	125 g/4½ oz	228	0	12	42	16	2–4
Beans, kidney, cooked	90 g/3¼ oz	112	0	7	20	5	2–4
Beans, navy, cooked	90 g/3¼ oz	127	0	7	24	10	2–4
Beans, pinto, cooked	85 g/3 oz	122	0	7	22	7	2–4
Beans, runner, green, cooked	125 g/4½ oz	44	0	2	10	4	2–4
Beans, runner, yellow, cooked	125 g/4½ oz	44	0	2	10	4	2–4
Beans, white, cooked	90 g/3¼ oz	125	0	8	23	5	2–4
Beans, white, small, cooked	90 g/3¼ oz	127	0	8	23	9	2–4
Beef, eye of the round	85 g/3 oz	170	7	24	0	0	2–4
Beef, flank	85 g/3 oz	180	9	23	0	0	2–4
Beef, mince, 95% lean, raw	85 g/3 oz	145	6	22	0	0	2–4
Beef, rump	85 g/3 oz	160	6	26	0	0	2–4
Beef, topside	85 g/3 oz	158	5	27	0	0	2–4

Food Item	Serving Size	Calories	Fat	Protein	Carbs	Fibre	Cycle
Beetroots	1 beetroot	35	0	2	8	4	2–4
Black-eyed beans, cooked	175 g/6 oz	160	1	5	34	8	2–4
Bread, cracked wheat	1 slice	65	1	2	12	1	2–4
Bread, pitta	55 g/2 oz	150	1	3	30	0	2–4
Bread, pumpernickel	1 slice	75	1	3	15	2	2–4
Bread, rice bran	30 g/1 oz	69	1	3	12	1	2–4
Bread, white	1 slice	70	1	2	13	1	3–4
Breadfruit	220 g/7¾ oz	235	3	7	7	7	2–4
Broad beans, cooked	170 g/6 oz	187	1	13	33	9	2–4
Broccoli, cooked	155 g/5½ oz	55	0	4	11	5	1–4
Brussels sprouts, cooked	155 g/5½ oz	56	1	4	11	4	1–4
Buckwheat groats, roasted, cooked	85 g/3 oz	77	0	3	17	3	2–4
Bulgar wheat, cooked	90 g/3¼ oz	160	0	5	34	4	2–4
C							
Cabbage, all varieties	70 g/2½ oz	17	1	1	4	2	1–4
Carrots	1 medium, 60 g/2¼ oz	65	0	1	15	4	1–4
Cashews	30 g/1 oz	157	12	5	9	1	3–4
Cauliflower, cooked	125 g/4½ oz	29	0	3	5	3	1–4
Celery, raw	100 g/3½ oz	14	0	3	1	2	1–4
Chard	175 g/6 oz	7	0	1	1	1	1–4
Cheese, Brie	55 g/2 oz	190	16	12	2	0	3–4
Cheese, Camembert	55 g/2 oz	180	14	10	0	0	3–4
Cheese, Cheddar, lowfat	55 g/2 oz	98	4	14	1	0	3–4
Cheese, cottage, 2% fat	115 g/4 oz	101	2	15	4	0	3–4
Cheese, Edam	55 g/2 o.	202	16	14	1	0	3–4
Cheese, Emmenthal, reduced fat	55 g/2 oz	101	3	16	2	0	3–4
Cheese, feta, reduced fat	55 g/2 oz	117	7	12	2	0	3–4

Food Item	Serving Size	Calories	Fat	Protein	Carbs	Fibre	Cycle
Cheese, fontina	55 g/2 oz	221	18	15	1	0	3–4
Cheese, goat	55 g/2 oz	256	20	17	1	0	3–4
Cheese, goat, semisoft	55 g/2 oz	206	17	12	1	0	3–4
Cheese, mozzarella, reduced fat	55 g/2 oz	144	9	14	2	0	3–4
Cheese, parmesan, grated	2 tablespoons	43	3	4	0	0	3–4
Cheese, Parmigiano Reggiano, grated	2 tablespoons	40	3	4	0	0	3–4
Cheese, ricotta, light	125 g/4½ oz	120	5	10	6	0	3–4
Cheese, Roquefort, reduced fat	55 g/2 oz	49	2	1	8	0	3–4
Cheese, string. light	1 string	50	3	6	1	0	3–4
Cherries, sour	8 pieces	30	0	1	7	2	3–4
Cherries, sweet	8 pieces	30	0	2	7	2	3–4
Chicken breast, w/o skin	½ breast	130	2	27	0	0	1–4
Chicken, dark meat, w/o skin	140 g/5 oz	287	14	38	0	0	4
Chicken, light meat, w/o skin	140 g/5 oz	214	6	38	0	0	1–4
Chicken, poussin, meat only	1 bird	295	9	51	0	0	2–4
Chickpeas, cooked	165 g/5¾ oz	269	4	15	45	13	2–4
Chicory	1 head	87	1	6	17	16	1–4
Clams, steamed or boiled	150 g/5½ oz	138	2	24	5	0	2–4
Cold cereals, All-Bran	90 g/3¼ oz	160	2	8	46	20	3–4
Cold cereals, All-Bran Bran Buds	90 g/3¼ oz	140	2	4	48	26	3–4
Cold cereals, Fibre One	60 g/2¼ oz	120	2	4	50	28	3–4
Cold cereals, gluten-free	¾ cup	200	3	7	42	6	3–4
Corn, sweet, white	1 ear	77	1	3	17	2	2–4
Corn, sweet, yellow	1 ear	77	1	3	17	2	2–4
Courgette	1 medium	46	0	2	10	1	3–4

Food Item	Serving Size	Calories	Fat	Protein	Carbs	Fibre	Cycle
Couscous, cooked	160 g/5½ oz	176	0	6	37	0	2–4
Crab, canned	135 g/4¾ oz	134	2	28	0	0	2–4
Crab, cooked	1 crab	140	2	28	1	0	2–4
Crab, king, raw	1 leg	144	1	32	0	0	2–4
Crackers, melba toast	35 g/1¼ oz	129	1	4	25	2	4
Crackers, rye	1 cracker	37	0	1	9	3	4
Crackers, wheat	1 cracker	60	9	0	0	1	4
Crackers, wholemeal	1 cracker	18	1	0	3	0	4
Cranberries	100 g/3½ oz	44	0	0	12	4	1–4
Crayfish, wild	8 crayfish	21	0	4	0	0	2–4
Cress, raw	50 g/1¾ oz	16	0	1	3	1	1–4
Cucumber	1 cucumber	45	0	2	11	2	1–4
Cucumber, peeled	120 g/4¼ oz	14	0	1	3	1	3–4
Currants, black	115 g/4 oz	71	1	2	17	0	3–4
Currants, red and white	115 g/4 oz	63	0	2	16	5	1–4
D							
Dandelion greens	55 g/2 oz	25	0	2	5	2	1–4
E							
Egg, hard-boiled	135 g/4¾ oz	211	14	17	2	0	1–4
Egg, poached	1 medium	74	5	6	0	0	1–4
Egg, scrambled	220 g/7¾ oz	365	27	24	5	0	1–4
Egg noodles, cooked	80 g/2¾ oz	107	1	4	20	1	3–4
Egg substitute, liquid	1 tablespoon	13	1	2	0	0	1–4
Egg white, raw	1 medium	17	0	4	0	0	1–4
Elderberries	145 g/5 oz	106	1	1	27	10	1–4
Endive, frisée	30 g/1 oz	41	1	3	9	7	1–4
F							
Fennel	85 g/3 oz	27	0	1	6	3	3–4
Figs	1 medium	37	0	0	10	2	3–4
Figs, dried	1 fig	21	0	0	5	1	3–4
Fish, black cod	85 g/3 oz	166	13	11	0	0	1–4
Fish, bluefin tuna	85 g/3 oz	122	4	20	0	0	1–4
Fish, butterfish	85 g/3 oz	124	7	15	0	0	1–4
Fish, carp	85 g/3 oz	108	5	15	0	0	1–4
Fish, catfish	85 g/3 oz	81	2	14	0	0	1–4

Food Item	Serving Size	Calories	Fat	Protein	Carbs	Fibre	Cycle
Fish, cod, Atlantic	85 g/3 oz	70	1	15	0	0	1–4
Fish, croaker, Atlantic	85 g/3 oz	88	3	15	0	0	1–4
Fish, haddock	85 g/3 oz	74	1	16	0	0	1–4
Fish, halibut	85 g/3 oz	94	2	18	0	0	1–4
Fish, herring, Atlantic	85 g/3 oz	134	8	15	0	0	1–4
Fish, herring, Pacific	85 g/3 oz	166	12	14	0	0	1–4
Fish, mackerel, Atlantic	85 g/3 oz	174	12	16	0	0	1–4
Fish, mackerel, king	85 g/3 oz	89	2	17	0	0	1–4
Fish, mackerel, Pacific	85 g/3 oz	134	7	17	0	0	1–4
Fish, mackerel, Spanish	85 g/3 oz	118	5	16	0	0	1–4
Fish, monkfish	85 g/3 oz	65	1	12	0	0	1–4
Fish, ocean perch, Atlantic	85 g/3 oz	80	1	16	0	0	1–4
Fish, perch, mixed species	85 g/3 oz	77	1	17	0	0	1–4
Fish, pike, northern	85 g/3 oz	75	1	16	0	0	1–4
Fish, plaice	85 g/3 oz	77	1	16	0	0	1–4
Fish, pollock, Atlantic	85 g/3 oz	78	1	17	0	0	1–4
Fish, rainbow smelt	85 g/3 oz	82	2	15	0	0	1–4
Fish, red mullet	85 g/3 oz	99	3	16	0	0	1–4
Fish, red snapper	85 g/3 oz	85	1	17	0	0	1–4
Fish, rockfish, Pacific	85 g/3 oz	80	1	16	0	0	1–4
Fish, roe, mixed species	1 tablespoon	20	10	3	0	0	1–4
Fish, salmon, farmed	85 g/3 oz	156	9	17	0	0	1–4
Fish, salmon, wild	85 g/3 oz	121	5	17	0	0	1–4
Fish, sea bass, mixed species	85 g/3 oz	82	2	16	0	0	1–4
Fish, sea trout, mixed species	85 g/3 oz	88	3	14	0	0	1–4
Fish, shad	85 g/3 oz	167	12	14	0	0	1–4
Fish, skipjack tuna	85 g/3 oz	88	1	19	0	0	1–4

Food Item	Serving Size	Calories	Fat	Protein	Carbs	Fibre	Cycle
Fish, sturgeon, mixed species	85 g/3 oz	89	3	14	0	0	1–4
Fish, tilapia	85 g/3 oz	108	2	22	0	0	
Fish, trout	85 g/3 oz	126	6	18	0	0	1–4
Fish, white sucker	85 g/3 oz	78	2	14	0	0	1–4
Fish, whitefish	85 g/3 oz	114	5	16	0	0	1–4
Fish, wolf fish	85 g/3 oz	82	2	15	0	0	1–4
Fish, yellow fin tuna	85 g/3 oz	93	1	20	0	0	1–4
G							
Garlic	1 clove	4	0	0	1	0	1–4
Grapefruit	½ fruit	50	0	1	12	3	1–4
Grapes, red	75 g/2½ oz	106	0	1	28	1	1–4
Grape vine leaves	4 leaves	11	0	1	2	0	3–4
Guavas	1 fruit	37	1	1	8	3	3–4
H							
Hazelnuts, dry roasted	30 g/1 oz	183	18	4	5	3	3–4
J							
Japanese soba noodles, cooked	115 g/4 oz	113	0	6	24	2	3–4
Jicama	130 g/4½ oz	46	0	1	11	6	3–4
K							
Kale	65 g/2¼ oz	34	1	2	7	1	1–4
Kefir, low fat, natural	240 ml/8 fl oz	120	2	14	12	3	1–4
Kiwi	1 medium	45	0	2	11	5	3–4
Kohlrabi, cooked	165 g/5¾ oz	29	0	2	7	1	3–4
Kumquats	1 fruit	13	0	0	3	1	3–4
L							
Lamb, leg, shank half	85 g/3 oz	156	9	15	0	0	2–4
Lamb, leg, sirloin half	85 g/3 oz	222	18	15	0	0	2–4
Lamb, loin, choice, raw	85 g/3 oz	237	18	15	0	0	2–4
Leeks	1 leek	54	0	1	13	2	1–4

Food Item	Serving Size	Calories	Fat	Protein	Carbs	Fibre	Cycle
Lemons, with peel	1 fruit	22	0	1	12	5	1–4
Lentils, cooked	200 g/7 oz	230	1	18	40	16	2–4
Lettuce, green leaf	30 g/1 oz	5	0	1	1	1	1–4
Lettuce, iceberg	70 g/2½ oz	10	0	1	2	1	1–4
Lettuce, red loose-leaf leaf	30 g/1 oz	3	0	0	0	0	1–4
Lettuce, romaine/cos	50 g/1¾ oz	8	0	1	2	1	1–4
Limes	1 fruit	20	0	1	7	2	1–4
Linseed oil	1 tablespoon	120	14	0	0	0	1–4
Lobster, raw	1 lobster	135	1	28	1	0	2–4
M							
Macadamia nuts	30 g/1 oz (10–12)	203	22	2	4	2	3–4
Mangoes	1 fruit	135	1	1	35	4	3–4
Margarine, fat-free spread	1 tablespoon	6	0	0	1	0	3–4
Mayonnaise	1 tablespoon	100	11	0	0	0	3–4
Mayonnaise, light	1 tablespoon	50	5	0	0	0	3–4
Milk, buttermilk, cultured, reduced fat	240 ml/8 fl oz	137	5	10	13	0	3–4
Milk, nonfat, powder	25 g/1 oz	82	0	8	12	0	3–4
Milk, semi-skimmed	240 ml/8 fl oz	138	5	10	14	0	3–4
Milk, skimmed	240 ml/8 fl oz	102	2	8	12	0	3–4
Millet	200 g/9 oz	756	8	22	146	17	2–4
Miso soup, reduced sodium	125 ml/4 fl oz	273	8	16	36	7	1–4
Muesli, lowfat	60 g/2¼ oz	190	2.5	4	40	3	3–4
Mushrooms	70 g/2½ oz	15	0	2	2	1	1–4
Mushrooms, enoki	1 large	2	2	0	0	0	1–4
Mushrooms, oyster	1 large	55	1	6	9	4	1–4
Mushrooms, portobello	1 large	0	0	0	0	0	1–4
Mushrooms, shiitake	1 mushroom	11	0	0	3	0	1–4

Food Item	Serving Size	Calories	Fat	Protein	Carbs	Fibre	Cycle
Mussels, raw	150 g/5½ oz	129	3	18	6	0	2–4
Mustard, ready-prepared, yellow	1 teaspoon	3	0	0	0	0	1–4
Mustard greens	55 g/2 oz	15	0	2	3	2	1–4
N							
Nectarines	1 fruit	60	0	1	14	2	1–4
O							
Oat bran	50 g/1¾ oz	118	3	8	31	7	2–4
Oats, porridge, instant, prepared w/water	120 g/4¼ oz	65	1	3	11	2	2–4
Oil, canola	1 tablespoon	124	14	0	0	0	3–4
Oil, olive	1 tablespoon	119	14	0	0	0	1–4
Oil, sesame	1 tablespoon	120	14	0	0	0	3–4
Oil, vegetable, walnut	1 tablespoon	120	14	0	0	0	3–4
Okra	100 g/3½ oz	31	0	2	7	3	1–4
Onions, sweet	1 onion	106	0	3	25	3	1–4
Oranges	1 large	86	0	2	22	4	1–4
Oyster, raw	85 g/3 oz	69	2	8	4	0	2–4
P							
Papaya	145 g/5 oz	55	0	1	14	3	3–4
Parsley, dried	1 teaspoon	1	0	0	0	0	1–4
Parsley, fresh	60 g/2¼ oz	22	1	2	4	2	1–4
Parsnips	135 g/4¾ oz	100	0	2	24	7	2–4
Pasta, corn, cooked	140 g/5 oz	176	1	4	39	7	3–4
Pasta, plain, cooked	150 g/5¼ oz	197	1	7	40	2	3–4
Pasta, spinach, cooked	150 g/5¼ oz	195	1	8	38	2	3–4
Peaches	1 large	61	0	1	15	2	1–4
Peanuts, dry roasted w/salt	30 g/1 oz	166	14	7	6	2	3–4
Pears	1 pear	121	0	1	32	7	1–4
Pears, Asian	1 pear	116	1	1	29	10	1–4
Peas, green, fresh, cooked	160 g/5⅔ oz	134	0	9	25	9	2–4
Peas, green, frozen, cooked	160 g/5⅔ oz	125	0	8	23	9	2–4

Food Item	Serving Size	Calories	Fat	Protein	Carbs	Fibre	Cycle
Peas, split, cooked	200 g/7 oz	231	1	16	41	16	2–4
Pecan nuts	30 g/1 oz (20 halves)	196	20	3	40	3	3–4
Peppers, chilli, green	150 g/5½ oz	29	0	1	6	2	3–4
Peppers, chilli, red	1 pepper	18	0	1	4	1	3–4
Peppers, jalapeño	1 pepper	4	0	0	1	0	3–4
Peppers, sweet, green	1 medium	24	0	1	6	2	1–4
Peppers, sweet, red	1 medium	31	0	1	7	2	1–4
Peppers, sweet, yellow	1 medium	32	0	1	8	1	1–4
Pheasant, breast, without skin	85 g/3 oz	113	3	21	0	0	3–4
Pineapple	1 fruit	227	1	3	60	7	3–4
Pistachio nuts	30 g/1 oz (49 kernels)	161	13	6	8	3	3–4
Pitta bread, wholegrain	1 pitta	170	2	6	35	5	3–4
Plantains	1 medium	218	1	2	57	4	3–4
Plums	1 fruit	30	0	1	8	1	1–4
Polenta	60 g/2¼ oz	220	2	2	24	1	2–4
Pomegranates	1 fruit	105	1	2	26	1	3–4
Popcorn, air-popped	8 g/¼ oz	31	0	1	6	1	3–4
Pork, loin, centre loin, cooked	85 g/3 oz	199	11	22	0	0	2–4
Pork, loin, sirloin, cooked	85 g/3 oz	176	8	24	0	0	2–4
Pork, loin, tenderloin, cooked	85 g/3 oz	147	5	24	0	0	2–4
Pork, loin, top loin, cooked	85 g/3 oz	192	10	24	0	0	2–4
Pork, loin, whole, cooked	85 g/3 oz	211	12	23	0	0	2–4
Potatoes	1 medium	164	0	4	37	5	2–4
Potatoes, jacket, w/skin	1 medium	160	0	4	37	4	2–4
Potatoes, jacket, w/o skin	1 medium	143	0	3	35	3	2–4
Potatoes, red	1 medium	153	0	4	34	4	2–4
Potatoes, white	1 medium	149	0	4	34	5	2–4
Poussin	1						3–4

Food Item	Serving Size	Calories	Fat	Protein	Carbs	Fibre	Cycle
Prawns, mixed species, raw	1 medium prawn	6	0	1	0	0	2–4
Prunes, unsweetened	4 prunes	100	0	1	24	3	1–4
Pumpkin	115 g/4 oz	30	0	1	8	1	2–4
Pumpkin, canned	245 g/8²/₃ oz	83	1	3	20	7	2–4
Q							
Quail, breast, without skin	85 g/3 oz	105	3	19	0	0	3–4
Quinoa, cooked	95 g/3¼ oz	127	2	5	24	2	2–4
R							
Radicchio	40 g/1½ oz	9	0	1	2	0	1–4
Radishes	115 g/4 oz	19	0	1	4	2	3–4
Raspberries	125 g/4½ oz	64	1	2	15	8	1–4
Rhubarb	125 g/4½ oz	26	0	1	6	2	3–4
Rice, basmati	95 g/3¼ oz	140	2	3	31	2	2–4
Rice, brown	95 g/3¼ oz	127	1	3	27	2	2–4
Rice milk	240 ml/8 fl oz	120	3	1	23	0	3–4
Rice, wild	80 g/2¾ oz	83	0	3	17	2	2–4
Rocket	20 g/¾ oz	4	0	1	1	0	1–4
S							
Salad dressing, 1000 island	1 tablespoon	58	6	0	2	0	3–4
Salad dressing, bacon and tomato	1 tablespoon	49	5	0	0	0	3–4
Salad dressing, blue cheese	1 tablespoon	77	8	1	1	0	3–4
Salad dressing, Caesar	1 tablespoon	78	9	0	1	0	3–4
Salad dressing, coleslaw	1 tablespoon	61	5	0	4	0	3–4
Salad dressing, French	1 tablespoon	71	7	9	2	0	3–4
Salad dressing, honey Dijon	1 tablespoon	58	5	1	3	1	3–4
Salad dressing, Italian	1 tablespoon	43	4	0	2	0	3–4
Salad dressing, light varieties	2 tablespoons	23	2	0	1	0	3–4
Salad dressing, mayonnaise	1 tablespoon	103	12	0	0	0	3–4

Food Item	Serving Size	Calories	Fat	Protein	Carbs	Fibre	Cycle
Salad dressing, peppercorn	1 tablespoon	76	8	0	1	0	3–4
Salad dressing, ranch	1 tablespoon	25	0	0	0	0	3–4
Salad dressing, Russian	1 tablespoon	76	8	0	2	0	3–4
Salsa, without oil	2 tablespoons	15	0	0	4	0	1–4
Sauce, pasta	250 g/9 oz	185	6	5	28	1	1–4
Sauce, salsa	260 g/9¼ oz	70	0	4	16	4	1–4
Sauce, soy	1 tablespoon	10	0	0	0	0	1–4
Sauce, steak	1 tablespoon	25	0	0	6	0	1–4
Sauce, teriyaki	1 tablespoon	15	0	17	2	0	1–4
Sauce, Worcestershire	1 tablespoon	13	0	0	3	0	1–4
Sauerkraut	70 g/2½ oz	25	0	1	5	4	3–4
Sausage, turkey	1 link, 30 g/ 1 oz	67	5	4	.5	0	3–4
Scallops	1 scallop	26	0	5	1	0	2–4
Shallots	1 tablespoon, chopped	7	0	0	2	0	1–4
Soya beans, green, cooked	90 g/3¼ oz	254	12	22	12	7	2–4
Soya beans, nuts, roasted, dry	45 g/1½ oz	194	9	17	14	3	3–4
Soya burger	1 patty	125	4	13	9	3	1–4
Soya milk	240 ml/8 fl oz	127	5	11	12	3	3–4
Spaghetti, spinach, cooked	140 g/5 oz	182	1	6	37	2	1–4
Spaghetti, whole wheat, cooked	140 g/5 oz	174	1	7	37	6	1–4
Spinach	30 g/1 oz	7	0	1	1	1	1–4
Spring greens	55 g/2 oz	11	0	1	2	1	1–4
Spring onions	50 g/2 oz	18	0	1	4	2	1–4
Squash, summer, e.g. courgette, croockneck, straightneck	115 g/4 oz	18	0	1	4	1	3–4
Squash, winter, e.g. acorn, butternut, hubbard, spaghetti	115 g/ 4oz	39	0	1	10	2	2–4
Squid, mixed species, raw	30 g/1 oz	26	0	4	1	0	2–4

Food Item	Serving Size	Calories	Fat	Protein	Carbs	Fibre	Cycle
Stock, beef	240 ml/8 fl oz	31	0	5	3	0	1–4
Stock, chicken	240 ml/8 fl oz	86	3	6	9	0	1–4
Strawberries	150 g/5½ oz	49	1	1	12	3	1–4
Sunflower seeds	1 tablespoon	47	4	2	2	1	3–4
Swedes	140 g/5 oz	50	0	2	11	4	3–4
Sweet potato	135 g/4¾ oz	114	0	2	27	4	2–4
T							
Tangerine	1 large	52	3	2	6	0	3–4
Taro, cooked	65 g/2¼ oz	94	0	0	23	3.4	2–4
Tofu, firm	125 g/4½ oz	183	11	20	5	3	1–4
Tofu, soft	125 g/4½ oz	76	5	8	2	0	1–4
Tomato passata, bottled	250 g/9 oz	95	1	4	22	5	1–4
Tomato purée, canned	130 g/4½ oz	107	1	6	25	6	1–4
Tomatoes, canned, chopped or crushed	240 g/8½ oz	82	1	4	19	5	1–4
Tomatoes, green	180 g/6¼ oz	41	0	2	9	2	1–4
Tomatoes, orange	180 g/6¼ oz	25	0	2	5	1	1–4
Tomatoes, red	180 g/6¼ oz	32	0	2	7	2	1–4
Tortilla, wholegrain, 25 cm/10 in	1 tortilla	120	5	2	16	1	3–4
Turkey bacon	2 slices	70	5	4	0	0	3–4
Turkey, breast, skinless, meat only, roasted	115 g/4 oz	153	1	34	0	0	1–4
Turkey, dark meat, skinless, meat only, roasted	115 g/4 oz	183	5	33	0	0	4
Turkey, white meat, cooked, sliced	30 g/1 oz	30	1	5	1	0	1–4
Turnip greens	55 g/2 oz	18	0	1	4	2	1–4
Turnips	130 g/4½ oz	36	0	1	8	2	2–4
V							
Veal cutlet	85 g/3 oz	128	3	24	0	0	2–4

Food Item	Serving Size	Calories	Fat	Protein	Carbs	Fibre	Cycle
W							
Walnuts	30 g/1 oz (14 halves)	185	19	4	4	2	3–4
Watercress	35 g/1¼ oz	4	0	1	0	0	1–4
Watermelon	150 g/5½ oz	46	0	1	12	1	3–4
Wine, red	100 ml/3½ fl oz	74	0	0	2	0	3–4
Wine, white	100 ml/3½ fl oz	70	0	0	1	0	3–4
Y							
Yakult	1 bottle	50	0	0	0	0	1–4
Yam	150 g/5½ oz	177	0	2	42	6	2–4
Yoghurt, fruit, low fat	225 g/8 oz pot	118	0	6	24	0	1–4
Yoghurt, fruit, full-fat milk	225 g/8 oz pot	250	6	9	38	0	1–4
Yoghurt, natural, low fat	225 g/8 oz pot	110	4	8	7	0	1–4
Yoghurt, natural, full-fat milk	225 g/8 oz pot	138	7	12	11	0	1–4